20°
N.

120°   140°

INDO-
CHINA

Gulf
of
Siam

MALAY
PENINSULA

South China Sea

Sulu
Sea

PHI

Pacific
Ocean

Celebes Sea

BORNEO

SUMATRA

Java Sea

KRAKATOA

JAVA

Strait of Makassar

CELEBES

Flores Sea

Banda Sea

NEW
GUINEA

0°

DUTCH   EAST   INDIES

TIMOR

Timor Sea

AUSTRALIA

20°
S.

N

W   E

S

120°   140°

KRAKATOA

KRAKATOA

Rupert Furneaux

PRENTICE-HALL, INC.
ENGLEWOOD CLIFFS, N. J.

PRENTICE-HALL INTERNATIONAL, INC., *London*
PRENTICE-HALL OF AUSTRALIA, PTY., LTD., *Sydney*
PRENTICE-HALL OF CANADA, LTD., *Toronto*
PRENTICE-HALL OF INDIA (PRIVATE) LTD., *New Delhi*
PRENTICE-HALL OF JAPAN, INC., *Tokyo*
PRENTICE-HALL DE MEXICO, S.A., *Mexico City*

Contents

KRAKATOA

1.   Opening Salvo

THE PLATE slid off the table and crashed to the floor, smashing into a thousand pieces. Mrs. Van der Stok contemplated the ruin of her delft dinner service in disgust. It was part of her dowry, a cherished possession. Years before she had brought it intact across eleven thousand miles of ocean to Batavia when her husband was appointed director of the observatory. In the next room Dr. Van der Stok was disturbed by the rattling and banging of the doors and windows of the house. Looking at his watch he noted the time, 10.55 a.m. Putting down the copy of the Java *Bode* he had been reading, he went on to the verandah. From the distance came a low rumbling, the not unfamiliar sound of an erupting volcano. The sun was shining brightly, the day hot and humid, not a cloud in the sky. The booming sounded like distant artillery, and it appeared to come from the northwest which was strange, for Java's many active volcanoes lay mostly to the south. Even though it was Sunday it was his duty to investigate. Walking to his observatory, Dr. Van der Stok inspected the instruments. The pointer of the magnetic needle of the seismograph showed no deviation, only a trembling motion in a perpendicular direction. Its quivering was absolutely vertical; there were no horizontal tremblings. The vibrations continued for longer than would have been the case had they resulted from an earthquake. Going outside he lay down and put his ear to the ground. There was absolutely no subterranean noise. The drumming noise, the rattling of doors and windows, and the destruction of his wife's prized dinner plate were not caused by an earthquake, that was certain. Somewhere a volcano

9

must be in eruption. Dr. Van der Stok entered his observations
in the official diary under the date, May 20th, 1883.

The distant rumbling went on all day. Dr. Van der Stok
timed each explosion. In Batavia, Dutchmen and natives
flocked into the streets, disturbed by the noises which were
both loud and soft, and by the rattling and banging of doors
and windows. The Dutch were not particularly disturbed;
volcanic eruptions were part of life in the East Indies. The
natives were frightened. They whispered that the mountain
ghost, *Orang Aljeh,* was on the prowl. They kept their voices
low, because the Dutch disapproved of their superstitions.

Telegrams despatched from Batavia to towns and villages
throughout Bantam—Java's northern province—brought no definite news. The drumming noise had been heard everywhere,
but no one knew from whence it came. Dr. Van der Stok
was perplexed. Java only extended a hundred miles or so to
the northwest. Then came the Sunda Strait, a narrow channel
of sea dividing Java from Sumatra. The noises came from the
northern island, he surmised; a quite likely possibility, for
Sumatra, like Java, was part of the most volcanic region of the
world. During the period of European colonisation, since 1602
when the Dutch first came to Java, the two islands had been
devastated by many frightful eruptions. Native legends told of
still earlier catastrophies. In Java alone there were forty-nine
active volcanoes.

The telegrams from Batavia reached towns lying on the
shores of the Sunda Strait. At Merak, at its eastern end, K. A.
Naumann, the overseer in charge of the Chinese labourers who
were quarrying stone for the harbour works at Batavia, had
nothing to report in reply to the query from his chief, Herr
Van Boose. The day was warm and sunny, its stillness broken
only by the rumblings which he could not locate. Across the
channel at Kalimbang on the Sumatra shore Mrs. Beyerinck,
the young wife of the Dutch controller, was indulging in her
favourite pastime, reclining on her verandah and watching the
big ships go by on what she was told was one of the world's
greatest highways, the sea link between the Indian Ocean and

the China Seas. "We were much bothered by the sounds and tremors that Sunday morning," she wrote later. They lasted all day, and the tremors were best observed in the bathroom where the surfaces of the water barrels were continuously in motion. The rumbling noise appeared to come from the south, from the Java shore, but nothing unusual could be seen. A number of ships were navigating the Straits, their white sails glinting in the sun, their smoke hanging lazily in the brilliant sky.

At Anjer, the chief port on the Java shore, the watering place for ships passing through the Straits, Mr. Schruit sat on the verandah of the small hotel owned by the Lloyd's agent. Schruit had recently been appointed telegraph master at Anjer, and he had left his wife and young children in Batavia while he sought a home for them. He regretted the separation; but it was only temporary, he hoped. That Sunday morning he was idly watching the ships go by through the agent's telescope. The Dutch mail packet *Zeeland* was displaying an unusual number of flags, but he couldn't make out the message they conveyed. He was about to put down the telescope, when he heard several loud reports and the hotel was shaken as if by a giant's hand. Through his telescope Schruit swept the Straits. He could see nothing unusual. The ships sailed on. The Sumatra coast loomed in a green haze, thirty miles distant.

Away to the west the little island group of Krakatoa, in the centre of the Straits, rose in his vision. The telescope enlarged each of its three islands in turn. First came Lang, or Long Island, with Verlaten, or Desert Island, slightly behind and to its left, and between them and stretching further to the southwest, the main island of Krakatoa, rising to 2,700 feet—three humble little peaks dwarfed by the majestic volcanic mountains soaring into the heavens along the Java and Sumatra coastlines. The sky above Krakatoa was clear. No cloud rose above its three tiny hills. Schruit did not expect to see any. Krakatoa never smoked, never shook. There wasn't a better behaved mountain in the whole of the East Indies. Calm and peaceful, Krakatoa rose from the sea, a mass of greenery, clothed from base to summit in luxurious growth of forest and tropical vegetation, a landmark for ships coming from the west, the first sight of verdure to break the monotony of three thousand miles of ocean. True, there were vague native legends of a great eruption two hundred years before when the sea had been choked with pumice, and of an even greater catastrophe in the dim past. These stories were discounted by Dutch officials. Krakatoa was an extinct volcano, a burnt-out crater, sleeping and slumbering in its old age. Schruit's gaze passed on.

Had radio then been invented, several ships nearby could have told a different story. As it was, some time elapsed before their reports were published. The *Zeeland*, steaming towards the Indian Ocean, passed within five miles of Krakatoa. Steam and debris were being vomited from the northern cone, and her crew heard a rattle like artillery. The needle of the ship's compass oscillated violently, spinning round and round. The American brig *A. R. Thomas* sailed even closer, her decks becoming covered with a thin layer of ash. Captain Hollman, master of the German naval corvette *Elizabeth*, saw a vast dome-shaped cloud of vapour rising above the islands to a height he estimated at thirty-six thousand feet. As it billowed up, the dark cloud was vividly lit by flashes of fire, flickering around the pillar of steam. It was accompanied by heavy detonations, and showers of yellow ash fell on the vessel's decks, percolating everywhere.

As that Sunday, May 20th, progressed, rumblings and bangs were heard throughout the Sunda Strait and far beyond to a distance of 250 miles, and the gigantic cloud of vapour and ash rising above Krakatoa became visible to the thousands of people, native and Dutch, who inhabited its shores. Fishermen did not dare put to sea and peasants abandoned their occupations to stand gazing at the awesome spectacle. At Kalimbang, Mrs. Beyerinck was told by her native servants that the bangs and ash came from Krakatoa, a story she disbelieved. It is a burnt-out crater, she informed them. *Antoe*

Laoet, the sea ghost, lives there, they warned her. Mrs. Beyer-inck, for all her disbelief, shivered. Only a few weeks before, she remembered, she had read a frightful story of an island engulfed by a tidal wave.

Captain Walker of the barque *Actea,* 150 miles west of the Sunda Strait noted in the ship's log that the sky to the east was a peculiar light green, and to the northeast there was "a dark blue cloud which reached from the horizon to the zenith." At 2 p.m. it became quite dark, visibility falling to one hundred yards. He thought it was a rain cloud, until fine dust fell on the vessel, covering its rigging, decks and seamen's clothes. That night the sun looked a dull silver ball as it sank below the horizon.

A telegram despatched from Anjer at 4 p.m. told the Government officials at Batavia: "Krakatoa casting forth fire, smoke and ash accompanied by explosions and distant rumbling." The message cleared up the mystery, but it raised no fears. Krakatoa was extinct and innocuous.

The detonations and clouds of steam continued for a week. Several ships passing through the Straits remarked about the phenomena. On May 21st, Captain Hollman on the *Elizabeth,* now 345 miles west of Krakatoa, noticed the sky was a dome of opaque glass, the sun suspended in the void like a pale blue globe, its light percolating through the veil of dust in the manner of an eclipse.

On that Monday afternoon, eight fishermen from Sebessi, another island in the Straits, came to report to the controller of Kalimbang that they had been over to Krakatoa in their proa to get wood for building. They told Mr. and Mrs. Beyerinck that as they walked into the forest rising from the beach they had heard cannon fire and had remarked that "there must be a warship in the neighbourhood." They went on felling trees until they heard another bang. This made them curious and they ran to the beach. Hardly had they reached it when the earth burst open at their feet, throwing up stones and ash. They fled as fast as they could and swam to a small island, one to which they could normally have waded. Now the tide was high and they had great difficulty in getting back to their proa.

Mrs. Beyerinck told her husband not to let the men fool him. An eruption, she pointed out, could not begin on the beach. The controller replied he had thought of that too, but no amount of questioning would shake the men's story. An hour later Mr. Beyerinck had an opportunity to test it for himself. The Resident of the Lampong district arrived by boat with orders from the Governor-General at Batavia to go to Krakatoa. Sailing over to the islands, which were in Mr. Beyerinck's department, the two officials saw with their own eyes that the fishermen's story was true. Near the beach, the earth was belching fire and smoke. The Resident telegraphed Batavia that Perboewatan, the northernmost of Krakatoa's three cones, was active, a report which was confirmed by the Resident of Bantam who quoted his native assistant as saying that the sounds were similar to the noise of an anchor chain being raised.

The mail packet *Zeeland,* which Mr. Schruit had watched through his telescope, called at Java Head on Monday evening. From here her captain, Commandant Mackenzie, telegraphed a message to the Java *Bode* which published it next morning. He had passed close to Krakatoa on Sunday, and he and his passengers and crew were amazed by the phenomena of nature. Above the island hung a dark heavy cloud out of which came a series of flashes, accompanied by unbroken cracklings like nonstop machine-gun fire. Around the island the sea was rising in waterspouts. It became so dark he was forced to proceed at half speed, although he was anxious to leave the area as quickly as possible. The air did not begin to clear until 3 a.m., and when dawn broke next day he saw that the whole vessel was covered with thick ash and the decks were strewn with lava and pumice, some pieces as large as hen's eggs.

Next day, May 22nd, the Dutch mail steamship *Soenda* passed within two miles of Krakatoa. Her medical officer, Dr. Sulzer, watched a column of ash and steam rising above the islands. From its base issued every few minutes fiery red clusters shaped like sheaves of wheat. These were accompanied by loud reports that made the vessel tremble. He noticed a new crater on the west coast of the new island, from which spurted dark red fire, and he felt the heat radiating on his face and hands. The sea was coated with pumice, and for half an hour heavy showers of ash fell on the ship's deck. When, thirty miles from the islands, he ordered a sailor to lower a bucket into the sea, it brought up pumice only and hardly a drop of water.

The Queensland Royal Mail steamer *Archer* also encountered a field of floating pumice that night, and she steamed through showers of ash for seven hours. Next day Captain Grainger told newspaper reporters at Batavia he could feel the heat of the eruption on his hands and face at a distance of two miles. Captain Ross, of the Dutch barque *Haag,* informed officials at Anjer that the forest on Krakatoa's slopes was on fire. The master of the Netherlands packet *Conrad* told a similar story. His ship had been delayed five hours by the sea of pumice. The temperature had risen ten degrees while the ship was enveloped in the belt of ash which filled the eastern end of the Straits where the monsoon stopped it dead like a wall.

Reports poured into Batavia from a wide area. The explosions had been heard as far away as Singapore, 522 miles distant, and a scientifically minded Englishman, Botanist H. O. Forbes, wrote from Timor, 1,350 miles away, to say that a sprinkling of ash was falling outside his hut. From the coasts of the Sunda Strait came daily reports of Krakatoa's renewed activity. The Governor-General of the Dutch East Indies ordered A. L. Schuurman, a mining engineer, to visit Krakatoa.

The *Gouveneur General Loudon,* with Schuurman, a photographer named Hamburg and eighty-five sightseers on board, left Batavia in the evening of May 26th. Before quoting from Mr. Schuurman's report it is advisable to describe the Krakatoa island in greater detail.

Krakatoa is both the name of the group and that of the chief island on which rose in 1883 three old volcanic cones: Rakata

(2,700 feet), Danan (1,460 feet) and Perboewatan (400 feet), in that order running from southwest to northeast. The island was five miles long and from three to one mile wide. The other two islands, Lang and Verlaten, were smaller and there was also a rocky island named Polish Hat. None of the islands was inhabited. The volcanic activity in May, 1883, derived from Perboewatan.

The *Loudon* reached Anjer at midnight from where Schuurman observed an intermittent glow on the horizon in the direction of Krakatoa. Every few minutes there was a burst of light from which fell a rain of fire. When dawn broke on May 27th, a Sunday, he saw a broad pillar of cloud towering into the sky and drifting away to the north. As the *Loudon* neared Krakatoa, Schuurman remarked that it looked very strange. Instead of rich tropical vegetation there was nothing but arid barren waste from which smoke was rising as from a furnace.

> Only the peak (Rakata) still showed some green, but the southern slope was smothered with a thick layer of grey ashes from which arose an occasional withered and twisted tree trunk bereft of branches or leaves, like naked spectres, meagre remains of the thick, impenetrable forest which had until recently covered the island. From the middle of this dark and desolate countryside, the epitome of total destruction, a powerful column of smoke of indescribable beauty drifted over the sea, several tens of metres in width at its base. This column was hurled into the sky with the crash of thunder to a height of 3,000 feet when it became paler and paler as it abandoned its cinders to the east wind which let them fall in the form of a blanket.

This was the foreground to the tableaux. It left Schuurman with the thought that the column of black and silver cloud was only a feeble indication of the furious battling of the elements that had produced it. The ash column emitted an appalling noise and periodically let fall a rain of stones which, from the ship, seemed like dark points darting about in the air.

As the *Loudon* approached closer, Schuurman noticed that

Verlaten Island was covered with grey ash, giving the impression of a wintry countryside. The rain of ash had fallen also on Lang; but its greenery had not quite disappeared, and some beautiful trees were still standing on the islet of Polish Hat. The lofty cone of Rakata showed no signs of activity, but its slopes were wrecked and covered with pumice.

Captain Lindemann of the *Loudon* put a boat at Schuurman's disposal and he landed on the northern beach of the main island, immediately below the cone of Perboewatan. On the sand lay a band of pumice stones a foot thick, and they were covered by a layer of ash two feet deep. The party of sightseers climbed the slopes, walking over the ash into which they sank as far as their calves. Schuurman reports:

> Following the tracks of the most courageous, or perhaps the most stupid, we climbed inland with no further obstacle than the ashes which gave under our feet, the route being over a hill from where we could see, emerging from the ash, some broken tree trunks showing signs that their branches had been violently stripped off. The wood was dried, but nothing indicated that it had been alight or smouldering.

He found no leaves or branches, which led him to suppose that the de-timbering of the island was probably due to a violent wind, such as is frequently produced by volcanic eruptions.

As the party ascended the cone of Perboewatan the crackling and grumbling column of cloud rose above them. To one visitor it appeared like a gigantic spectral cauliflower evolving in successive stages of growth before his eyes. From time to time immense funnels formed, into which the incessantly changing ravelled wreaths of smoke were sucked. The column rose to several thousand feet. It was drifting eastwards, spreading out into mist and discharging ashes which reminded the spectator of the dark fringes of a rainstorm seen on the horizon. As the sightseers climbed higher and higher both ground and air became warmer and the evidence of destruction more conspicuous. At two hundred yards from the summit they en-

countered sulphur troughs out of which mud boiled up in enormous bubbles which burst.

Finally, they reached the crater itself. From it rose opaque clouds lit by a red glow. Around the crater steam was escaping from a number of crevasses and fissures. Schuurman looked into the crater, which he estimated at 3,300 feet in diameter at the top and narrowing to 150 feet at the bottom. It was 500–800 feet deep, and its bottom was covered with a black, shiny crust from which columns of ash and pumice were being thrown up. Against his advice some of the more adventure-some climbed a little way down into the crater, from where they brought up pieces of pumice and lava as mementos of their visit to Krakatoa.

These less scientifically minded sightseers were enthralled by the grandeur of the spectacle, the ascending column of steam whirling upwards with a terrific roar, its sides revolving with ash and stones which were vainly trying to break out, but were constantly being pushed back while they were borne upwards and around and around. Peering into the crater the visitors were impressed by the seething lava, rent every few minutes by explosions. During one of the explosions a member of the party discharged a rifle, afterwards likening its report, as compared with the din made by the explosion and the hurtling aloft of ejected fragments, to "the popping of a champagne cork amid the hubbub of a banquet." Another equally picturesque-minded spectator likened the sound to the snapping of a cracker bonbon in the midst of the hilarity of a banqueting hall.

Schuurman was more concerned with the products of the explosion. The ash, he found, was fine grained and greyish in colour, composed of colourless glass mingled with fragments of rock. The pumice interested him most. This was composed of tiny fragments, some only the size of a bead. They were very fragile, which indicated they were in a high state of tension. Chemical tests conducted on his return to Batavia dis-closed that the specimens contained 65 percent SiO_2 (silica).

Before the party sailed from the island, Hamburg took a

remarkable photograph. A rendering of it appears in the photo section of this book.

As the *Loudon* steamed away darkness fell, and the spectacle was one of extraordinary beauty and grandeur. The lower part of the ash column was a mass of glowing red from which darted tongues of yellow flame. Red-hot stones drove fierce furrows into the air and, falling back to earth, were shattered into a thousand pieces.

On the day of the *Loudon's* visit to the island, the Dutch naval vessel *Sumatra* took soundings close to Krakatoa. There was no raising of the sea bed. Four days later, on May 31st, the ship *Bitang*, passing nearby, was suddenly shaken by a disturbance which her captain attributed to a quake on the sea bottom. Tremors were reported from several places on the shores of the Sunda Strait.

After May 27th, the volcanic activity of Perboewatan declined, and there was a lull until June 16th when for five days a thick black cloud hung over the islands. When it was driven away by the east wind, columns of steam were seen to be rising, not from Perboewatan but from Danan, the central crater; and the renewed activity continued during July. During that month several acute observers passed through the Strait. H. O. Forbes, on his voyage to England from Timor on board the *Quetta*, noticed extensive pumice. Some pieces were as big as a child's head, and were covered with barnacles. The P. and O. liner *Siam*, on a voyage from King George Sound (Western Australia) to Ceylon, encountered a sheet of pumice seven hundred miles west of Sumatra. It was floating in lanes from five to ten yards wide.

Early in July, the Liverpool barque *Hope*, 178 days out from Newport, South Wales, entered the Straits and a young seaman on board had his first glimpse of Krakatoa. When the *Hope* called at Anjer for orders, Dalby was given shore leave and with two other seamen he made an evening trip by canoe along the coast. Speaking on the radio fifty years later he recalled the Javanese hinterland as a real paradise, "a profusion of vegetation rising from the seashore to the summit of hills several thousand feet high." The atmosphere impressed him with mystic awe. The land and sea breezes were at rest, and it was enhanced by the subtle scent of the spice trees and the sweet yet weird and melancholy chant of some natives paddling their canoe close to the dark shore. Resting on their paddles, the English sailors watched a long straight column of ash cloud rising from Krakatoa's peak. Next day the *Hope* sailed for Saigon. Six weeks later she was back at the eastern entrance to the Straits.

On July 3rd, geologist and mining engineer R. D. M. Verbeek passed through the Straits on his return to Batavia from Europe. Two months later he landed on the shell of Krakatoa, as the scientific historian and officially appointed observer of the great eruption, the Big Bang of which was heard over one-thirteenth of the surface of the earth, and which awakened geologists to the terrific pent-up forces lying inside the earth's crust.

Krakatoa was visited again on August 10th by H. J. G. Ferenzaar, chief of the Bantam Clearing Brigade, who sailed across the Strait in a native boat and landed alone. He found it too dangerous to carry out a detailed survey, but he made a drawing. The islands were completely devastated. Only a few tree trunks remained and these were denuded of branches and leaves. The ground was covered with a layer of ash mixed with sulphur, two feet thick. From the summit of Danan rose columns of ash cloud, pinkish grey in colour. He judged it imprudent to explore the peak of Rakata, from which columns of steam were now rising, as well as from eleven other foci of eruption.

Between August 14th and 23rd, four ships, the *Madura*, the *Loudon*, the *Bay of Naples* and the *Princess Whilhelmina*, reported thick darkness, explosions, rains of ash and seas of pumice in the Straits. From Kalimbang in Sumatra the appearance of Krakatoa was seen to be greatly changed; the conspicuous summit had disappeared.

To the Dutch officials and colonists Krakatoa's renewed activity was no more than a nine days' wonder. The volcano had roused itself after two hundred years of sleep. It had fumed, flashed and thundered. No one realised that placid little Krakatoa was the most dangerous volcano on the face of the earth.

Krakatoa's three months of menacing prelude were over. Nature's three-ringed circus was about to open. The subterranean fires were being stoked; the boiler was about to burst. Deep beneath the islands lay a white-hot chasm, Nature's crucible of death.

Above ground, along the shores of the Straits, 36,417 people worked and slept, ate and drank, fought and loved, unaware that they would shortly become victims of Nature's greatest catastrophe, the world's biggest bang, in comparison with which Mr. Khrushchev's 60-megaton bomb would have sounded like the "pop" of a toy pistol.

2. Raging Demon

U NKNOWN AND unsuspected, Krakatoa was nearing the climax of its second volcanic cycle. The volcano's history has been reconstructed by the many Dutch geologists who have studied its rocks and strata.

Long ago, in remote prehistoric but in a comparatively recent geological epoch, a giant cone grew up by slow eruption and accretion, by the outflow and accumulation of molten matter that wells up from deep down in the earth's crust through fissures and pipes formed by the cracking, arching and sagging of the surface.

Exactly what happens in the depths below is still partly a mystery; one which volcanic eruptions are helping to solve.

Inside the earth's mantle—the 1,800-mile layer beneath the 20-mile deep crust—physical and chemical processes generate intense heat which melts the rocks in the upper part of the mantle, their various constituents dissolving and merging.

The enormous pressure exerted by the rocks above, which at a depth of forty miles is reckoned to be not less than one hundred tons per square inch, keeps these rocks solid. Otherwise they would be completely molten; for mining and oil drilling operations show that temperature increases at an average of 100° Fahrenheit per mile, reaching at that depth a degree of heat at which the rocks would melt at surface level. Vibrations caused by earthquakes, which cannot pass through liquid, prove that for tens and hundreds of miles downwards the interior of the earth is rigid. Its core, geologists think, is slowly cooling and shrinking. The outer shell responds by bending, breaking and crumbling. Howell Williams, professor of geology at the University of California, likens the process to the skin of a baked apple, wrinkling as it cools. As the earth's crust cracks, the pressure on the deep-seated material below is relieved. The rocks melt and the molten material rises towards the surface through cracks and fissures. It squeezes aside the adjacent overlying rocks to form a chamber, a reservoir of red-hot rock, where it is imprisoned.

The resulting "melt," as it is called, can be either "basic," that is nonacid, or "acid," even extremely acid, depending upon the composition of its constituents. The term "acidity" is used by geologists to indicate the relative percent of silica, SiO_2. Which the melt is, will affect the volcano's behaviour and how it erupts.

Basic or nonacid melts are called "basaltic," where the silica content is less than 50 percent. Where the silica content is more than 66 percent they are called "granitic." The intermediate stages are named "andesitic," after the typical volcanic products of the Andes Mountains of South America.

There are, of course, many intermediate stages, and the layers of the melt may vary in acidity as they become contaminated both by mixture and by the caving in of the sides of the reservoir (or chamber) and the volcano's chimney.

Although not quite technically correct, in as much as it describes the relative percent of silica, we can perhaps best understand the term "acidity" as implying the viscosity, the stickiness of the molten material in the melt. Acid melts (those of high silica content) are viscous and sticky, whereas basic melts are more fluid. The stiffness or fluidity of the melt influences the ease with which gas, the motivating force of all volcanic eruptions, is liberated.

Gas is formed from a variety of sources, including water which either seeps from above or is generated from below. The water, from wherever it comes, joins the molten matter, a mixture of silicates which is called "magma." It contains a variety of gases of which water is usually the most abundant. As the result of the release of confining pressure, the water vapourises and becomes steam. It expands a thousandfold.

The turbulent gas-charged magma is forced upwards by the weight of the earth's crust bearing down from above. It pushes its way through fissures and cracks, and blasts a channel towards the earth's surface. How it finds its way out depends upon the magma's viscosity.

If the magma is very "basic," that is, very hot and fluid, the gases escape easily, and the lava (the liquid product) flows away undramatically like honey, doing little damage except to objects in its path, and finally solidifies in the form of tongues and sheets which may extend for a few yards or many miles, and may be a few inches or thousands of feet in depth. The Hawaiian volcanoes are examples of this type of mild eruption.

If, on the other hand, the magma is very acid, that is, thick and sticky, it is difficult for the gas to escape. The magma may force its way out of the vent in the form of spurting lava sprays, or it solidifies and plugs the chimney. Pressure builds up from below.

When the pressure of the gas-charged magma exceeds that exerted by the plug in the chimney, it blows out with explosive violence, like the uncorking of a champagne bottle. The result may be negligible or terrible, depending upon the quantity and nature of the magma expelled, and the location of the volcano. The more acid the magma, the greater its explosiveness, the greater the danger of catastrophe.

The magma is ejected in the form of lava and pumice, and as cinders and ash. Pumice is the characteristic product of the explosive expansion of acidic magmas in which the high gas content causes the magma to froth as it rises in the chimney, being shattered into tiny particles by explosion. The explosion may wreck and engulf the volcano and cause widespread devastation and loss of life.

Or the debris, ejected in the form of flowing lava (in a mild eruption) or exploded as pumice, rock, cinders and ash (in a semi-violent eruption), accumulates round the vent, or vents, building, as time goes by and the process is repeated, a cone or cones which may even grow into a mighty mountain.

Krakatoa's original hypothetical cone grew up by slow accumulation, by this mountain-building process, becoming a tooth in the 1,000 mile arc of 500 volcanoes (117 of which are still active) that straddles Sumatra and Java, one of the most unstable regions of the earth's surface. Its volcanoes are built of andesite rock and their magma is of great viscosity, because of its considerable acidity—its power to solidify, in laymen's terms.

By Pleistocene times, a half-million years ago perhaps, Krakatoa's cone soared 6,000, 10,000, even 20,000 feet in the air. Its base was 25 miles in circumference and it partly filled the area now occupied by the Sunda Strait.

Some time in the latter part of the Pleistocene period Krakatoa reached the climax of its first volcanic cycle. Its highly acidic magma clogged and exploded. Vast quantities of fresh magma surged to the surface, blowing out and emptying the reservoir beneath, and causing a void into which the mighty cone collapsed and was engulfed.

A similar catastrophe, in which some seventeen cubic miles of material disappeared, occurred more recently in Oregon, *Mt. Mazma* U.S.A., creating Crater Lake which now measures 6 miles across and is 2,000 feet deep.

Krakatoa's great paroxysm may have been witnessed by Java apeman, Pithecanthropus, whose skull cap was found in 1891 at Trinil by Professor Eugène Dubois. Though unlikely, it is just possible that these erect-walking apemen and their descendants may have passed down a confused memory of their terrible experience, for early Javanese legends relate a catastrophe that seems to be derived from such an awe-inspiring event, one that did not recur until 1883.

The engulfment of the original cone left a "caldera," a cauldron-shaped depression, a sea basin of unknown depth. On the outer fringes of this basin grew up, from submarine vents from which new magma spurted and welled, three small surface cones, Perboewatan, Danan and Rakata, which finally merged into one island. Beside it, Lang and Verlaten islands grew also from the debris ejected from these cones.

The new "cone-building" process was under way. The under-lying basaltic magma reached the surface at first uncontami-nated; but as time went on it assimilated, as it rose, sialic material, becoming more and more acid, more and more vis-cous, and increasingly dangerous

Various legends may relate to the period of Krakatoa's re-growth.

The Javanese *Book of Kings* states that in the year 338 Saka, or A.D. 416, a thundering noise was heard from the mountain Batuwara (now called Pulosari, one of the extinct volcanoes nearest the Strait of Sunda). This was answered by a similar noise from Kapi, lying westward of modern Bantam, Java's most northerly province, which seems to imply that Krakatoa is meant. From it a great sheet of fire reached the sky. The whole world was shaken with violent thunderings that were accompanied by heavy rains of stones. The noise was fearful. With a tremendous roar Kapi burst into pieces and sank into the depths of the earth. The sea rose and inundated the land; its inhabitants drowned. The water subsided but the land on which Kapi stood became sea, and Java and Sumatra were divided into two parts.

When this event occurred is unknown. Professor N. P. Berg surmises on philological grounds that the legend is derived from the first Sudanese immigrants who witnessed these events about 250 B.C., but this seems improbable. Geologists can find no evidence of a grand collapse, which the legend describes so graphically, between the original engulfment and 1883. The Sunda Strait may not have become completely navigable until a thousand or more years ago, and its existence was not known to sailors until A.D. 1175.

Perboewatan, Danan and Rakata must have erupted both mildly and semi-violently repeatedly during their many thou-sands of years of cone-building, at the culmination of which they reached the heights of 400 feet, 1,460 feet and 2,700 feet respectively. Their magma was becoming increasingly acidic and new vents were opened, liberating pressure below, and allowing the gases to rise to the surface. The first-named two cones were in eruption in 1680-1681, as two Dutch travellers record.

Johann Wilhelm Vogel, an assayer of the silver mines at Salida and a servant of the Dutch East India Company by whom he was known as a pious and sober young man, passed through the Straits in July, 1679. He saw nothing of note. On his return journey on February 1, 1681, he noticed with great astonishment that the island of "Cracketouw" which "on my first journey to Sumatra appeared so very green and gay with trees, now lay altogether burnt up and waste before our eyes and spewed out fire from great fire holes." On enquiry to the ship's captain, Vogel was told the eruption had occurred in May, 1680. The captain said, according to Vogel:

> The former year and when he was on his voyage to Bengal, he had met with a great storm, and about ten miles from the island he encountered an earthquake on the sea, followed by frightful thunderings and crackings, from which he imagined that an is-land or else a piece of land had burst up, and shortly afterwards as they drew a little closer with the ship to land and were come to the mouth of the Sunda Strait it was evident that the island of Cracketouw had burst out; and his conjecture was correct, for he and all the ship's company perceived the strong sulphur-atmos-phere, also the sea covered with pumice which they scooped up as curiosities.

Researches by Professor Berg in May, 1883, in the *Journal du Château de Batavia* confirmed that the captain of the *Zyp*, the ship on which Vogel sailed, made a voyage in the *Aden-borgh* to Bengal in 1680, thus attesting the story's authenticity, though the *Journal* itself makes no mention of Krakatoa's out-burst.

The other traveller, Elias Hesse, a mining engineer, who passed through the Straits on November 18, 1681, relates:

> The island of Cracketouw is uninhabited. It had about a year before broken out in eruption. It can be seen far at sea, when one is still many miles distant from it, on account of the con-tinually ascending smoke of the fire; we were with our ship very

close under the shore; we could perfectly well and accurately see
the wholly burnt out trees on the top of the mountain but not the
fire itself.

The officers and crew of the British naval ship, the *Discovery*, landed on Krakatoa in February, 1780, on their voyage
home after Cook's death in Hawaii. They found two springs,
one of fresh water from which they filled their casks, and
another of hot water in which the natives, who then inhabited
the island, bathed. They did not otherwise remark on the
island. Surveys of the island were made and charts were drawn
in 1849 and 1874, and R. D. M. Verbeek, on his visit in 1880,
drew some sketches.

Following its eighteen months' activity in 1680-1681, Krakatoa remained docile for two hundred years. The slow build-up
of pressure had been released, and the magma was not yet
sufficiently viscous and acid to clog and cause a violent explosion.

Krakatoa settled down into a well behaved volcano. The
peoples of the Sunda Strait became lulled into a false sense
of security, like the Roman legionnaires who built a camp on
the summit of Mount Somma, the explosion and collapse of
which in A.D. 79 destroyed Pompeii and Herculaneum; and in
the caldera of which Vesuvius subsequently arose, as had the
cones of Rakata, Danan and Perboewatan after Krakatoa's
first great paroxysm in Pleistocene times.

Krakatoa lay directly above a gigantic fissure in the earth's
crust, a line of structural weakness crossed by another fissure
immediately beneath the three tiny islands.

These cracks provided subterranean corridors from deep
beneath the earth's crust; easy escape routes for the huge mass
of gas-charged, highly acid magma now building up in the
white-hot chasm below, easy conduits for the downward seepage of sea water. The danger of catastrophe increased.

Between 1877 and 1880, the Strait of Sunda was rocked by a
succession of violent earthquakes; the one in September 1,
1880, was so violent that the upper part of the lighthouse on

Java's First Point was so badly damaged it had to be broken off and rebuilt.

These earth shocks and the mild eruptions of May–August, 1883, opened new cracks and vents, and widened old ones. Sea water oozed down into the magma chamber where on contact with the molten rock it became transformed into gas, its volume increasing enormously. The new vents provided channels for the release of the pressure building up below. The liberated gases rose in the volcano's chimney, the sticky magma frothing and bubbling.

During the early hours of Sunday, August 26th, the rising magma became clogged, the chimney plugged. In the depths below seethed a white-hot chasm, the melt, its pressure reaching bursting point.

At precisely 1 p.m. the raging magma frothed into pumice.

3. Fire Ring of the Pacific

THE NATIVE peoples of Java and Sumatra knew all about volcanoes. The explanation of their terrible outbursts was simple. Inside the earth lived a wicked spirit who, if he was not propitiated by proper sacrifices, made it tremble; and he expressed his rage by vomiting smoke and fire. A belief not far removed from that held by mediaeval Christian theologians who located hell's fires below the earth's crust and placed Queen Anne Boleyn's particular place of torment, for her sin in being the instrument of Henry VIII's apostasy from Rome, beneath Mount Etna in Sicily. No less remarkable conceptions of the nature of the interior of the planet are expressed by the adventures of Jules Verne's voyagers, in *A Journey to the Center of the Earth,* who descend the crater of Snaefell in Iceland, travel through devious passages and are thrown out of the crater of Stromboli in Italy on top of a column of rising lava. Even scientific opinion subscribed to the view that the earth was a molten mass covered by a thin outer shell through which lava spurted at certain places; a theory that was dispelled by the realisation that such an unstable planet, too flexible to be rigid, could not revolve in space. Nonetheless scientists made steady progress in their understanding of volcanic activity. By the eighteenth century they had swept aside many of the old myths and fancies.

Twentieth century geologists, invited to define a volcano, start usually by explaining what it is not. The ancients were in no doubt; volcanoes were burning mountains, the homes of the fire god. In Roman mythology Vulcan, the blacksmith of the gods, was the cause of the trouble; as he pounded his anvil fire and smoke rose from his workshop's craters. The island of Vulcano off the coast of Sicily was identified as his principal forge and given his name. The modern term "volcano" is derived from the Latin word.

The ancients had more reason to be terrified of volcanoes than we have today, for they did not understand the true cause of their activity. At one time in the dim, dark past, our planet was a mass of seething volcanoes, spewing out gigantic sheets of red-hot lava, building plateaus, island peaks and mighty mountains—their steam condensing into great oceans. As the earth's crust settled down, volcanic activity became localised into areas of structural weakness, the "youngest" regions, the Mediterranean Basin, the Atlantic fringe, the "fire ring" of the Pacific, the East Indies and West Indies—and these places are still the earth's soft spots.

Our inheritance of the classic tradition gives us greater knowledge of the Mediterranean volcanoes than of those located in more remote places. Scientifically clever as were the Greeks, they did not understand volcanoes. No one succeeded in doing so until the introduction of deductive reasoning, conceived by Francis Bacon and applied by the seventeenth century philosophers who, once the dead hand of religion had been removed, paved the way for the full investigation of nature.

Our knowledge, and subsequent understanding, of volcanoes begin with the letters of Pliny the Younger, which he wrote to the Roman historian Tacitus. Pliny, then a boy of eighteen, witnessed the eruption of Vesuvius in A.D. 79, in which his uncle lost his life and which overwhelmed the cities of Pompeii and Herculaneum.

The great Vesuvian outburst, the world's most famous volcanic eruption, is a story worth telling on its own account. It is doubly important in our study of Krakatoa's far greater catastrophic paroxysm, for it enables us to understand how modern geologists discovered what happened during the terrible twenty-two hours in which no mortal eye could discern the exact course of events.

In the days of the Caesars, the Bay of Naples was the playground of the Roman world—the resort of the most wealthy, the most famous and the most noble citizens of the Imperial City, who built patrician villas on its shores; and the rich fertility of the hinterland, its sinister cause unsuspected, brought a dense population. Towering over the bay rose the great mountain of Somma, its lurking dangers so unappreciated that Spartacus and his revolting gladiators encamped, in 72 B.C., within the lofty walls of the crater that filled its summit, an amphitheatre that provided a permanent camp for the legionnaires who drove him out; a crater formed, we know now, by a catastrophic outburst in which the primeval cone was engulfed.

No one suspected that Somma, which we now call Vesuvius, was a volcano, not even the poet Virgil who passed his declining years in Naples and who located in the bay the vestibule to the underground realms of the gods and giants, the place of smoke and fire, of cavernous recesses, of scorched rocks and subterranean passages. Other writers of antiquity observed indications of previous volcanic activity. Diodorus Siculus noticed that the mount had given forth fire in ancient times, and geographer Strabo stumbled upon the explanation of the district's fertility without detecting the meaning of the clue. The soil was so fertile that the giants had battled for its possession, he believed.

In the first century of the Christian Era, during the reign of the emperor Nero, the long dormant forces of Mount Somma reawakened. Geologists think that the volcano first emerged as an island, joining itself to the land by the eruption of material, and that it reached the end of its first cycle about ten thousand years ago, shortly after the end of the last Ice age, by terrific explosion and collapse. The wounds became healed, all memory of the disaster was forgotten and the mountain became recloaked in vegetation, so prolific that Spartacus and

younger Pliny's mother drew his attention to a cloud of very
unusual size and shape. The student was reading, but nonetheless he climbed to some rising ground to get a better view.
He saw an ascending cloud which he likened to the shape of a
pine tree "for it shot up to a great height in the form of a very
tall trunk, which spread itself out at the top into a sort of
branches, occasioned, I imagine, either by a sudden gust of
air that impelled it, the force of which decreased as it advanced upwards, or the cloud itself being pressed back again
by its own weight, expanded in the manner I have mentioned;
it appeared sometimes bright and sometimes dark and spotted,
according as it was either more or less impregnated with earth
and cinders."

Pliny's simile of a pine tree, a common feature of the Italian
landscape, to describe the cloud of steam rising above a volcano in paroxysmal eruption, has become the classic term;
one which has taken on even more sinister suggestiveness since
August 8, 1945, the fateful day when the first atomic cloud
rose above Hiroshima.

Pliny describes, by hearsay no doubt, his uncle's voyage of
mercy, the falls of hot cinders and pumice as his galley approached the mountain, and the sudden retreat of the sea as
he neared the shore. Finding the harbour of Resina, the port
of Herculaneum, blocked, Uncle Pliny sailed on to Stabiae
where he spent the night. Broad flames shone from the mountain, records the nephew, and villages on its slopes were burning. During the night the court of the house in which the
elder Pliny was resting became filled with ashes, and the villas
of the town were rocked from side to side by frequent concussions. The old man was roused and the whole company
took to the fields, their heads protected by pillows tied with
napkins, as a defence against the stones that fell about them.
Everywhere a deeper darkness prevailed than in the thickest
night. Reaching the seashore, the party was dispersed by flames
and smoke that were preceded by a strong whiff of sulphur.
Uncle Pliny fell to the ground. He tried to raise himself but
fell dead, suffocated, his nephew concluded, by some gross and

his men found vines by which they lowered themsel
the crater rim on the approach of Clodius's legions.

The first sign that the volcano was reaching a fres
came in A.D. 63 when, on February 5th, Pompeii, Herc
and Naples were shaken and damaged by a severe ear
spectacularly at the moment when Nero was giving a
in Naples, a rehearsal for his debut in Rome; a coi
which was not missed by historian Suetonius, no ad
the Julian dynasty, who remarked, "To be singing whi
vius thundered and fiddling while Rome burned was
fitting the Imperial madcap." During the next sixtee
the shores of the bay were shaken by earthquakes, not
usual foretaste of subsequent volcanic activity. On th
of August 23rd, '79, the shocks became more violent
Romans spent a sleepless night, among them the Plin
Elder a noted naturalist, and the Younger, a student li
Misenum on the northern tip of the bay with his uncle wl
manded the Roman galleys. Six years later the younge
replied to the request of Tacitus to describe his uncle's
The historian was concerned only with the last hou
famous man, and Pliny, in his reply, assumed apparent
Tacitus knew the chief facts of the eruption. We do no
if he did, for the volume in which he may have descr
was "lost" three hundred years later when, probabl
Christians censored it, amongst other Latin books, beca
its too realistic account of the early days of the Faith. In
ing as is Pliny's eyewitness description of the great v
outburst, it lacks therefore the details we might expec
omits all mention of the destruction of Pompeii, Hercula
the port to which Pliny the Elder sailed to rescue the
garrison, and Stabiae where he died; the first, six mile
the summit on the southeastern side, the second, nine
away near the seashore, and the third, down on the so
shore of the Bay.

About one o'clock in the afternoon of August 24t

---

* *Letters of Pliny* vi, 16.20. Tr. by William Melnoth, 1746.

noxious vapour. Next day his body was found without any
marks of violence, looking like that of a man asleep.

In a second letter, written in reply to the historian's request
for further information, the Younger Pliny describes his own
experiences at Misenum, twenty miles as the crow flies from
the erupting volcano. As August 24th advanced, a panic-
stricken crowd evacuated the town. Pliny followed, finding
himself in the midst of a most dangerous and dreadful scene.
The ground trembled so greatly that the chariots were agitated
backwards and forwards, and had to be supported by large
stones. The sea seemed to roll back on itself, the shore was
enlarged and several sea animals were left stranded. On the
land side rose a black and dreadful cloud, broken with rapid,
zigzag flashes, revealing variously shaped masses of flame, like
sheet lightning but much larger. The cloud descended and
covered the sea. The island of Capri and the promontory of
Misenum were lost to view. As Pliny and his mother sought to
escape, they were followed by a dense, dark mist that spread
over the country like a cloud. Fearful of being crushed to
death by the crowds, they turned from the main road.

Pliny's description of that awful night might have been
echoed by many of Krakatoa's victims, the thousands who did
not live to tell their stories:

> We had scarcely sat down when night came upon us, not such
> as we have when the sky is cloudy, or when there is no moon,
> but that of a room which is shut up and all the lights put out.
> You might hear the shrieks of women, the screams of children
> and the shouts of men; some calling for their children, others for
> their parents, others for their husbands, and seeking to recognise
> each other by the voices that replied; one lamenting his own fate,
> another that of his family; some wishing to die from the very fear
> of dying; some lifting their hands to the gods; but the greater
> part convinced that there were now no gods at all and that the
> final endless night of which we have heard had come upon the
> world. Amongst these there were some who augmented the real
> terrors by others, imaginary or wilfully invented. I remember
> some who declared that one part of Misenum had fallen, that

another was on fire; it was false, but they found people to believe them.

It now grew rather lighter, which we imagined to be rather the forerunner of an approaching burst of flames (as in truth it was) than the return of day; however, the fire fell at a distance from us, then again we were immersed in thick darkness, and a heavy shower of ashes rained upon us, which we were obliged every now and then to stand up and shake off, otherwise we should have been crushed and buried in the heap. I might boast that, during all this scene of horror, not a sign, or expression of fear, escaped me, had not my support been grounded in that miserable, though mighty consolation that all mankind were involved in the same calamity, and that I was perishing with the world itself. At last this dreadful darkness was dissipated by degrees, like a cloud or smoke; the real day returned, and even the sun shone out, though with a lurid light like when an eclipse is coming on. Every object that presented itself to our eyes (which were extremely weakened) seemed changed, being covered with deep ashes as if with snow.

Next day Pliny and his mother, her pace impeded by corpulence, returned to Misenum where they passed another anxious might alternating between hope and fear. The earthquakes continued, and frenzied people ran up and down heightening their own and their friends' calamities by terrible predictions. Pompeii was enveloped in pumice and ash to a depth of from fifteen to twenty-five feet, which killed many of its twenty thousand inhabitants and preserved the manner of their life as has been disclosed by the excavations which started in the eighteen century and continue still. Herculaneum was submerged by flowing volcanic mud sixty-five feet thick and, on cooling, became so hard that it makes excavation difficult. Tacitus records in his surviving Preface how "cities in the richest plains of Campagnia were swallowed up and overwhelmed." A century and a half elapsed before Historian Dion Cassius collected legends of the great eruption and recorded the tradition that the mountain had been torn asunder by huge giants. As time progressed all knowledge of the great catastrophe was lost and the cities of Pompeii and Herculaneum became forgotten. At both places new towns arose, their inhabitants unaware of the ancient cities buried beneath them.

The mountain has revealed a secret of its great paroxysmal outburst. The old cone of Somma disappeared. Where it went was for a long time a controversial problem, one that was finally set at rest by the disappearance of three-quarters of Krakatoa's principal island. Out of the crater left by the eruption of A.D. 79 grew a new cone. It was called Vesuvius and its name was given to the whole surrounding mountain. In the centuries that followed, Vesuvius erupted frequently, both mildly and in catastrophic outbursts. Following the eruption experienced by Pliny, which has given the title "Plinian" to violent volcanic outbursts, the summit became recloaked in trees and vines as Dion Cassius noticed in 203. Paroxysmal outbursts occurred in 472, 1036 and 1631, when six towns were destroyed and another nine were wrecked, the death roll being estimated at four thousand. Vesuvius has been in almost constant eruption since, and the outburst of 1872 is described as one of its greatest, the cloud of steam rising seven miles into the sky above the crater. In the eruption of 1906, one hundred thousand people were evacuated from Naples and 325 feet were lopped off the volcano's summit which rose previously to 4,338 feet above sea level. Vesuvius erupts a rare type of basalt called leucite, which is quite fluid, and its activity is both explosive and mild. Its occasional "Plinian" outbursts bring Vesuvius within the same classification as Krakatoa, with which the Italian volcano has one major feature in common— the total disappearance of its cone, a phenomenon that puzzled volcanologists for one hundred years.

The story of the rediscovery of Pompeii and Herculaneum has some bearing, in this connection, with the great eruption of Krakatoa. Despite suggestions made in the fifteenth and sixteenth centuries that search for these forgotten cities might be rewarding, nothing was done, although the construction of a canal that crossed the site of Pompeii revealed fragments of marble and coins bearing the image of the emperor Nero. A

century later search for water disclosed a tablet on which the
name of Pompeii was inscribed, but no excavations were under-
taken as a result of this pregnant clue. Meanwhile in 1710 an
Austrian army officer, the commander of the guard at the Court
of Naples, living near the town of Resina, acquired some unusual stones and statues from a peasant who found them while
digging a well, but no one identified the site as that of Herculaneum until, in 1738, three marble statues, the statue of a
horse in three pieces, and a plaque bearing the inscription
Theatrum Herculanensiem were discovered. By sheer luck the
excavators had chanced on the ancient theatre, the stage of
which had been decorated by statues. The rediscovery of Herculaneum led to a search for Pompeii at the town of Civita,
which was believed to lie above it. As the excavators dug
through the dried pumice, they uncovered streets and villas.
In one excavation they found the skeleton of a man from whose
hand had fallen a number of gold coins dating from the time
of Nero and Vespasian, the emperor, in A.D. 79.* Since then
half of Pompeii and parts of Herculaneum have been cleared.
Two thousand skeletons have been found at Pompeii, many
of them with their hands to their mouths, which suggests that
the town was overwhelmed suddenly—its people perishing by
suffocation from the fine dust or by asphyxiation from fumes.
Only thirty skeletons have been unearthed so far at Herculaneum, indicating, it is thought, that most of its population
had timely warning of the slow advance of the wall of mud and
lava which engulfed its houses and streets.

The excavation of these cities revealed a strange fact. The
cities and countryside were submerged many feet deep in lava
and pumice, the *products* of volcanic eruption. Only tiny fragments of the old cone of Somma were found, yet millions of
cubic feet had disappeared. In the nineteenth century two
opposing theories were advanced to explain this phenomenon.
For fifty years their protagonists clashed and argued.

Several other Italian and Sicilian volcanoes are almost as

---

* Died 23 June and succeeded by Titus.

famous as Vesuvius. They are located along the great earth fracture caused by the sinking of the Tyrrhenian Sea, and the rise of the Apennines in prehistoric times. Vulcano has been active from ancient times, its last notable eruption occurring in 1889–1890, its cone rising to 1,637 feet. It is mentioned by Herodotus about 475 B.C. and by Thucydides and Aristotle, and it has been identified as the island of Scylla, visited by Odysseus after the siege of Troy. Its great eruption in 1444 shook all Sicily, and another great outburst occurred in 1786. Its type of activity is similar to that of Vesuvius, beginning with explosive violence, vomiting pumice and ash, and then quietening down, but it does not, like Vesuvius, emit outflows of lava. Stromboli, the "lighthouse of the Mediterranean," another of the Aeolian islands, has been in eruption since Homer's day, and it is one of the few of the world's volcanoes in almost constant activity. It knows no repose and throws out incandescent fragments accompanied by clouds of steam uncontaminated by ash. Its cone rises to an elevation of 3,040 feet. From its submarine base it measures 10,400 feet. It is dwarfed, as European volcanoes go, only by Mount Etna in Sicily which towers 10,600 feet in the air. Both Pindus and Aeschylus sang of Etna's fiery outbursts and mighty power, and in Greek legends Zeus buried the rebel giant Typhon beneath its massive base, his struggles and convulsions accounting for its eruptions. Thucydides records one in 693 B.C., and Livy refers to three during the first and second centuries before Christ. Its outburst in 396 B.C., says Diodorus Siculus, brought a flow of lava twenty-four miles long and two miles wide which effectively stopped the Carthaginian army engaged in the Punic wars. Etna's most violent outburst in historic times occurred in 1669, reducing the summit by one thousand feet. In November, 1928, the lava flow destroyed the town of Mascali, and it is recorded as Etna's one hundred and twentieth major eruption since 693 B.C.

The study of volcanoes developed and advanced as superstition receded. During the Middle Ages scientific thought was constrained by religious doctrine; as late as 1689 the famous

Bishop Burnet declared that the earth had been created in a moment of time, in 4004 B.C. precisely; but within a century the beginning of earthly time had been extended to millions of years. Nineteenth century geologists, freed from the Christian dogma which decided that fossils were relics of Noah's flood, became fascinated by the Italian volcanoes and were not slow to perceive certain significant clues to the understanding of volcanic activity. They noticed that the distribution of the world's volcanoes seemed to coincide with regions most affected by earthquakes and that there appeared to be a "fire ring" of erupting volcanoes round the chief continents and oceans. They realised, too, that the clouds that rose above active volcanoes were composed of steam, and were not smoke, as had been thought for centuries. The detection of these clues led to certain conclusions, not all of them correct, and many controversies developed.

Water, particularly sea water, was believed to be the cause of volcanic activity. While it is now agreed that water is the trigger of eruptions, geologists still argue about its source, and the significance of the location of volcanoes in narrow belts along continental coastlines may be more apparent than real. Volcanoes, it is believed, are active in such regions because they are places of crustal weakness, where the folding and cracking of the earth's crust releases pressure and provides vents to the reservoirs below. A remarkable theory was advanced by Dr. Miguel Larreynaga of Guatemala in *Memoria sobre el Fuego de los Volcanos*. The sea, he thought, acted as a gigantic lens for the sun's rays, concentrating heat on the bottom of the ocean with such powerful force as to fuse the elements instantaneously and cause eruptions near seas and oceans.

Another controversy developed. Were volcanic edifices "elevated" by molten material rising from below, arching the earth's crust in great blisters or domes, or did they accumulate from material ejected from volcanic vents? The "crater-by-elevation" theorists reasoned that the conical shape of volcanic peaks proved they could not be due to the outpourings of

lava, because the streams were not continuous over all their
surfaces; and they observed that many volcanic cones rose
directly from the sea, reasoning that, as lava would solidify on
coming into contact with water, cones could not be built from
subterranean vents. The "crater-by-accumulation" theorists, on
the other hand, showed by actual observations that volcanic
edifices are the result of the accumulation of ejected debris;
and their opponents were forced to agree that lava rises from
below the earth's crust through vents that connect the surface
with the molten interior.

These arguments and debates led to the question, What is
a volcano? It perplexed geologists for a hundred years. Now
it is answered easily. A volcano is a hole in the ground through
which hot gas, molten material and fragmentary products rise
to the surface.

Gas, it is now agreed, is the active agent of volcanic action
and magma is its agent. Steam, expanding a thousandfold,
forces the magma up the chimney, or vent. What comes out of
a volcano depends upon the magma's viscosity. It takes three
forms, gas (largely steam), lava or pumice, and fragments
(some of which may be red-hot), which are called pyroclastic
materials from the Greek "pyro," fire, and "clastic," broken.
These solids can vary from huge blocks weighing many tons,
to dustlike particles so light they may drift in the upper atmosphere for years, and they may comprise cinders, ash or pumice.
Pumice is the characteristic product of highly explosive magma,
in which the high gas content causes the magma to froth as it
rises to the surface. When explosion occurs it is shattered into
particles, some as small as marbles, others as large as footballs,
and because of the air spaces formed by expanding gases,
pumice will float on water. Lava is the liquid product of
molten rock in which the acid content is low. The steam, which
is charged with various gases, erupts as water vapour, forming
often a cauliflower-shaped pillar of cloud which billows and
contracts and which may rise to many miles in height.

A glance at the map shows that volcanoes form a ring round
the Pacific Ocean, and geological surveys indicate that they

occur chiefly along young mountain systems such as the Alpine–Himalaya group and the Circum–Pacific ranges, the two great zones of crustal weakness. The Volcanic Survey of the world lists some 450 volcanoes that have been active in historic times, of which 275 are in the Northern Hemisphere and 155 in the Southern. Of these 336 are located in the Pacific half of the world and 94 in the Indo–Atlantic section. Of the 2,500 recorded eruptions, 2,000 have occurred in the Pacific area.

The world's volcanic zone starting from Europe begins with the recently extinct volcanoes of the Auvergne region of France and the Eifel area of Germany, and passes through the Alps (a new mountain system) down Italy to the central Mediterranean from where it continues through the islands of the Aegean Sea, to the Caucasus Mountains (where Ararat is the most prominent extinct volcano) and Persia. It carries on through the Himalayas from where it jumps to Burma and to Sumatra and Java where the intersection of the Alpine–Himalayan and Pacific systems results in the most volcanic region in the world. While one branch progresses southwards through the Lesser Sunda islands and the Moluccas to New Zealand, where there are four active volcanoes, the main stem swings northwards, along the western and northern Pacific seaboard, to the Philippines (eleven volcanoes), Japan (49 volcanoes), the Kurile islands (33 volcanoes), Kamchatka (20 volcanoes), Aleutians and Alaska (36 active vents). On the North American Continent the volcanic arc turns southward through the Cascade Mountains of Oregon (1 active) and proceeds to Mexico which contains 11 active craters. A branch loops eastward to the Lesser Antilles where the vents of Pelée and Soufrière are situated. The main stem continues on through Central America in three zones, having 31 volcanoes, down the Andes (19 volcanoes) to Chile, Argentina (22 cones) and to Antartica.*

Many Pacific island groups are also volcanic, notably Hawaii

---

* Numbers according to F. M. Bullard, 1962.

which contains four active cones. Another volcanic system crosses the Atlantic from north to south, commencing in Iceland, which has been described as the greatest lava field of modern times, and continues along a submerged ridge, its exposed peaks forming the islands of the Azores, the Canaries including the peak of Teneriffe, Cape Verde, St Helena, Ascension, and Tristan da Cunha from where the population had to be evacuated in 1962. Another volcanic system is found in eastern Africa, in the Great Rift Valley of Kenya, and in the extinct volcanoes of Mount Kenya and Kilimanjaro.

The activities of the Hawaiian and Icelandic volcanoes are remarkable because they are so different from Vesuvius and Krakatoa. The Hawaiian Islands are tiny dots in the mid-Pacific, the peaks of a volcanic range which have been built up from the sea bed by slow eruption and accumulation. Mauna Loa, the highest peak, rises 13,680 feet above sea level, 30,000 feet from the sea bed, the largest active volcanic edifice in the world. Mauna Loa and the other Hawaiian domes may have taken, if their present rate of mountain building has been their uniform pace, several million years to accumulate in the form of "shields," the word geologists use to explain their shape. In contrast with other Pacific volcanoes their magma is very basaltic, very hot and highly fluid, and it flows almost continuously from both Mauna Loa and Kilauea, the still active peaks. The Icelandic volcanoes are similar to those of Hawaii with one difference. Both are "shield" edifices, built by the slow accumulation of basaltic magma, but the Icelandic cones rise from long fissures rather than from central vents. In Iceland the hot volatile lava issues from cracks in the earth's crust and flows in sheets forming great plateaus. Heckla is the most famous Icelandic volcano. Twenty major outbursts have occurred since 1104, about the time the Norsemen discovered Iceland. The Laki fissure at Mount Skaptar erupted on June 8, 1783, directly and indirectly taking the lives of one-fifth of the island's population and killing half its cattle.

By 1880 geologists were acquiring considerable knowledge

of the historic outbursts of prominent volcanoes, but when a
survey of cones, active and extinct, was made in that year
Krakatoa was not listed as an active volcano, and it was not
included amongst the vents which form the "Fire Ring of the
Pacific," the Andesite Line as it is called.

4. Life on the Andesite Line

KRAKATOA'S OPENING prelude, harmless as it seemed, disturbed the simple agricultural and seafaring people who lived under the mountain's shadow. They watched the volcano's renewed activity with misgivings. The Dutch scoffed at their fears; there were far more dangerous volcanoes in Java and Sumatra. That could not be denied. Indonesia fairly bristles with volcanoes, both extinct and active. There have been volcanic outbursts in historic times, and an eruption of some sort occurs every three years. That is why Java is the most fertile region on the earth, for volcanic ash is a natural fertiliser. Java's enriched soil supports 1,200 people per square mile while Borneo, where there are no volcanoes, numbers only 4.5 people in the same space. Java has experienced several terrible volcanic catastrophies.

The eruption of Mount Merapi destroyed the Hindu–Javanese state of Mataram. How he recognised the volcanic cause of the sudden disappearance of this ancient kingdom has been explained by Professor R. W. van Bemmelen, who published his deductions in 1956 under the title *The Influence of Geological Events upon Human History*. Studying Java's past, van Bemmelen noticed that from about the year A.D. 1000, central Java had no history for six centuries, yet, previously, it had been the centre of a powerful kingdom whose rulers built many beautiful temples. Some of these had been left unfinished, and gave the impression that the craftsmen had been

45

forced to stop suddenly. The district rose to power again when
the second state of Mataram was founded by Moslems about
the year 1575. What was the cause of this long silence?

An ancient inscription, known as the Calcutta Stone because
it was carried to India in 1816 by Sir Stamford Raffles, dated
A.D. 1041, described the destruction of the kingdom in the year
928 Sakka, the equivalent of A.D. 1006. Historians took two
views about this inscription. Some thought its description of
the adversities suffered in central Java were symbolical only,
but others believed it recalled some natural calamity, such as
famine or volcanic eruption. One word of the old Sanskrit
seemed to denote the aftereffects of a catastrophic eruption.
The inscription recorded that after the catastrophe Java looked
like a "milk sea," and the same words were employed in Hindu
mythology to describe the period of chaos at the beginning of
time.

"Milk Sea," Geologist van Bemmelen knew, was an apt expression for the coating of ash and pumice frequently spread
by volcanic eruptions. Following this clue, he turned to examine Merapi, the southernmost and youngest mountain of the
volcanic range that straddles central Java. The volcano had
been in almost constant eruption since the sixteenth century,
but there were no records of its previous history. Working
under great difficulties, for he was a prisoner of war of the
Japanese, van Bemmelen made a geological survey of the
region. He distinguished two stages of growth on Merapi. The
original cone had collapsed and in its ruins a new cone had
grown. Calculating from historical data, old maps, and the
volume of material ejected from the volcano, van Bemmelen
established a cycle of activity and repose, at one to seven and
one to twelve-year intervals, which indicated that the old cone
had exploded and collapsed approximately nine and one-half
centuries before—about the year 1006. A catastrophic outburst
from Merapi could have given the death blow to the ancient
state, a conclusion to which the clue contained in the near
contemporary inscription so dramatically pointed.

About many of Java's great volcanic eruptions we know

little. In 1772, the cone of Papandayang was reduced from 7,034 to 3,000 feet in height by an eruption of "Plinian" intensity, leaving a crater 15 by 16 miles across; one of the most destructive outbursts in Javanese history, for it was accompanied by the eruption of two other volcanoes, 184 and 352 miles distant. Forty villages were "swallowed up by the opening of the ground," and 2,957 people were killed.

Tambora's eruption in 1815 may have equalled or even surpassed Krakatoa's sixty-eight years later. Situated on the island of Sumbawa, close to Java, Tambora burst into activity on April 5th, the detonations being heard for one thousand miles. Three distinct columns of flame were seen to rise to vast height, fiery lava streams flowed, and stones and pumice fell for miles, some pieces as large as a man's head. An area of three hundred miles was cloaked in darkness for three days and a whirlwind carried away house roofs and even men. The island's shoreline sank by eighteen feet. Twenty-six only of the island's 12,000 inhabitants survived the disaster, and according to some estimates 50,000 people perished on the mainland from starvation. Tambora ejected, it has been calculated, 36.4 cubic miles of matter, losing 4,100 feet in height and forming a crater 7 miles in diameter. The dust thrown into the atmosphere encircled the earth, darkening the sky and causing 1816 to be called "the year without a summer."

The Javanese had reason to be afraid of volcanoes. But on the face of it there seemed little cause for fear from Krakatoa, despite its roars and groans. It looked so small and peaceful, dwarfed by the many majestic peaks that dominated the Straits, Karang (4,500 ft.), Pulosari (4,000 ft.), Pajang (1,500 ft.), Princess Island (1,450 ft.), Sebessi Island (2,825 ft.) and Radjah Bassa (4,398 ft.), some of them giants compared with Krakatoa's 2,700 feet. No one suspected the terrible fires slumbering beneath Krakatoa's beauty. The Straits dwellers did not know that humble little Krakatoa lay at the weakest point on the Indonesian volcanic arc that rises to high altitudes in close proximity to deep sea troughs, on the fringe of the Andesite Line; the belt of acidic rocks which girdles the

Pacific, at a spot where gas-charged magma had been surging upwards for centuries, the siatic content of which had already reached the dangerously high level of 65 percent.

The natives knew the legends of Krakatoa's early catastrophic eruption when, according to ancient tradition, the Sunda Strait had been formed. "When 3,000 rainy seasons have passed away," Sumatra and Java will be reunited, they told each other in hushed whispers, repeating the prophesy passed down from father to son for countless generations. When the practical Dutch heard this saying, they pointed out that, as no one knew when the great eruption had occurred, the prophesy was valueless. They scoffed at the natives' fears, but they were curious about Krakatoa's name. How was it derived? they asked. They did not get a satisfactory answer and no one has succeeded in unravelling the mystery. There are several possible explanations.

According to one legend, the word "Krakatoa" is derived from the noise *Ka-krat-oa,* made by the white parrots that inhabited the island. Another story relates that one day an Indian prince passed through the Straits. Observing the island, he enquired its name. The vessel's master replied, "I don't know," employing the word *Kaga-tau,* the prince accepted that as the island's name. It seems more probable that the name is derived from the Sanskrit *karta, karkata,* and *karkataka,* which signify both "crayfish or crab" and the sign of the zodiac. This word implies that these crustaceans were found at the island, which is quite likely. Another interpretation derives the name of the island from the Malay *kelakatoe,* meaning "white-winged ant"; but its possible significance is difficult to understand unless we are to assume that it is based on the island's shape which could be so interpreted, especially if Lang and Verlaten islands had been seen covered in white pumice. On an old map, drawn before 1611, the island is called "Karata," which, it is believed, became corrupted into "Rakata," still the name of the island's chief peak. The original name was adopted by the Dutch who spoke it as "Krakatau."

Reassured by the superior knowledge of the white man, the

Javanese and Sumatran peasants and fishermen returned to their labours, as the Dutch hoped they would. Fatalistic and indolent, they took up their hoes and launched their proas, resuming their tranquil existence, the daily round of providing for the day which nature made easy for them. Their soil was fertile, the rivers and sea swarming with fish, the jungles rich in fruit and game. Until the eighteenth century no native needed to work very hard. The Dutch changed that. They forced their unwilling servitors to labour on plantations to grow the rich export crops, spices, sugar, coffee, tea and rice, which made huge profits.

When the Dutch reached the East Indies in the sixteenth century they found the islands inhabited by people of Malay race, the same as are found throughout Southeast Asia and Malaysia, Islamic by religion and Hindu in culture. Two thousand years before, the islands had been settled by traders and adventurers from China and India who drove the primitive inhabitants into the interior. Hinduisation lasted for fourteen centuries and its influence and religious beliefs have never been eradicated. Hindu and Buddhist temples survive still in the Javanese jungles, and these religions dominate life in the island of Bali.

Arab and Persian merchants, following the trade routes their ancestors had established a thousand years before, arrived in the thirteenth century; introducing Islam, the new religion spread rapidly. In 1292 Marco Polo set foot on Indonesian soil, the first European to reach the fabled spice islands. Portuguese, Spanish, English and Dutch seamen followed, and within a hundred years the Dutch had ousted all their rivals. Dutch rule was broken only between 1811 and 1816 by British occupation, when Sir Stamford Raffles, the founder of Singapore, ruled Java and Sumatra.

The Dutch found the Indonesians easy to manage. They preserved the ancient structure of Asiatic feudalism, governing the people indirectly through their own aristocracy. They installed the "Big Brother" system, whereby the native princes retained the semblance of power. At the side of each prince and headman stood a Dutch official, a Resident in each district, supported by assistant Residents and controllers. Everywhere Big Brother stood by his native counterpart, advising, supervising, directing and holding out his hand. The system worked well. The native Regents exploited the peasants and the Dutch overawed the Regents. The native rulers demanded "Master service" from their followers, so many days' work, so much produce; and the Dutch made fortunes. The workers did not complain. They paid great respect to rank and status. Rebellion was useless. The white rulers possessed guns, and they had none. The exploited people were not unhappy. Life in natives' paradise was easy. A bamboo house could be built in a day; a few hours' work sustained life. Articles the natives could not grow or make were supplied by Arab and Chinese traders who reaped a rich harvest from their trade, sufficient to carry them in pilgrimage to Mecca or home to mingle their bones with those of their ancestors. In his famous novel *Max Havelaar*, published in 1860, Eduard Dekker paints a candid picture of the oppression of the Javanese by their own sultans, under the fatherly eye of the Dutch. His book shocked opinion in Holland and led to drastic reforms, so that by 1883 the lot of the workers had been greatly improved.

The coastal dwellers on both shores of the Straits lived mostly in small communities ruled by headmen, in clusters of bamboo houses, roofed with palm thatch, high pitched and picturesque, each set in deep foliage, and surrounded by cultivated land—rice fields irrigated and tilled by the community. It is not possible to estimate accurately how many people lived along the coasts in 1883. The figures given in the Royal Almanac covered wider areas. In the Lampongs, the southern district of Sumatra, an area covering 10,000 square miles, there lived 70 Europeans, 128,939 natives, 255 Chinese and 154 Arabs. Bantam, Java's most westerly province, was inhabited by 360 Europeans, 565,438 natives, 1,479 Chinese and 21 Arabs. As most of these people drew their livelihood from the alluvial coastal plains or from the sea, it is reasonable to infer, as did an English visitor in 1883, that half of them at least lived under the shadow of Krakatoa—an island of evil reputation, apart from its volcanic dangers, for it had once been inhabited by pirates who carried off women from the mainland.

Bantam and the Lampongs were the two districts chiefly affected by Krakatoa's eruption. In both, low coastal plains are flanked by forest-clad hills which in Bantam advance and recede from the shore. The Bantamese shore was thickly studded with villages; the population was sparser in the Lampongs, a district subjugated by the Dutch in 1811. Both areas, lying within thirty to fifty miles of Krakatoa, were susceptible to inundation, particularly Lampong and Semanka bays, and the coastal strip on the southern shore between Merak, Anjer, Tjaringin, Pepper and Welcome bays. Telok Betong was the principal port of the Lampongs; Anjer of Bantam. There European ships called to water and pick up pilots. It stood at the mouth of a large river and the picturesque town was flanked by a wide semicircular valley, surrounded by a rampart of hills. The Rev. Tennyson-Woods gives this picture of Anjer in 1883:

European vessels generally stopped there to take a pilot, and new-comers were always delighted with the beautiful aspect of the bay. The shore was fringed by a close growth of cocoa-nut palms, backed by a dense shade of tropical fruit trees, such as jack fruit, mango and plantain. Amidst this foliage, solid white buildings with red-tiled roofs peeped out here and there. In the distance were two high volcanic ranges, lying north-east and south-east. The town was exceedingly pretty. Buried in shade, it was in a wide picturesque valley, while the Resident's house fronted a magnificent green esplanade beautifully shaded by the drooping branches of the warignen trees. The European residents were hardly more than 50, living, as in most Javanese towns, in picturesque tropical villas, enclosed with the usual Dutch gardens. But there was a large population otherwise. The town had a Chinese quarter, full of shops; an Arab quarter, somewhat like it, though smaller; and a very large campang of Javanese or Sudanese. Within a radius of five miles round Anjer some 20 populous campongs might be counted. Thus morning, noon and even night, the picturesque throng of market women, native officials, and the characteristic thatched carts with their pairs of bramin bulls or single buffaloes made the road a varied panorama of life and industry such as can only be seen in Java. Thus it was until the day of doom came, which turned all into a lifeless desert.

A great post road, built in 1830 at the cost of ten thousand lives, linked these coastal towns. At their eastern entrance the Straits narrowed, forming an elongated semieclipse, near to which lay the port of Merak. Further down the coast from Anjer stood Tjaringin, the residence of the local prince, a tiny port inhabited by six European households. These three towns, with Telok Betong, were to bear the brunt of Krakatoa's fury.

The morning of Sunday, August 26th, broke fine and clear. The sun rose high in the cloudless sky, promising another day of sticky, sickening heat. Vaporous hills swam and wavered in the misty heat. Low islands towered castlelike in floating mirage. Dark indigo-green plains sloped from jungle-clad hills, their glades flecked with sunlight and perfumed by exotic blooms, to shimmering pearly sea. From the west drifted a full-rigged barque, a mass of billowing white canvas; from the east chugged a steamer, its smoke trailing lazily in the opaque sky, its engines beating a gentle rhythm in the breathless air. Nature hung in hypnotic trance, chained in magic spell. From Krakatoa's three little cones rose faint whisps of steam. No one bothered with Krakatoa that lovely morning. At the entrance to the Straits several ships converged, their crews intent upon their voyages to Batavia and Singapore, Hong Kong and Cape Town, Boston and Liverpool. Across the sea wafted the slow beat of countless gamlan orchestras as the happy people of the land "where nature always wears a radiant smile" danced and sang.

In the depths below Krakatoa seethed a white hot chasm,
the Melt, its pressure reaching bursting point.

5. Paroxysm

THE PUMICE frothing in Krakatoa's chimney rose towards the plugs blocking the vents. The churning gases at the top of the magma column surged upwards. Down the length of the column the magma seethed and raged. Deep below, three miles down perhaps, in the reservoir itself, came a sudden generation of steam, too great for it to hold. The rising Demon struggled to free itself. For centuries it had churned and lashed, pushed and choked, seeking a way of escape. Long captivity would make the final discharge, when it came, the more terrible. Three solid plugs held it in check.

The stupendous volume of gas shot upwards—up the only escape route—up the chimney—up the vents of Perboewatan, Danan and Rakata, each cone sealed by plugs formed of fallen rock, ancient lava and fresh pumice.

For a time the pressure exerted by the plugs resisted the impelling force from below. The gases choked. Pressure built up. Tension increased.

The battle between the immovable object and the irresistible force was joined.

Below, the gases surged and climbed.

Above, the plugs squeezed and cracked.

The Demon pressed the attack.

Its searching fingers bored into the defences.

Spirals of gas corkscrewed into the cracking plugs.

The Demon fingers searched and probed.

The red-hot jets twisted and tore, drilling through the obstruction.

The Demon threw in all its power—the pent-up energies of time, the primeval forces that had built the earth's mountains, forged its valleys, levelled its plains, created its oceans.

The gas-rich magma mounted, thrusting the top layers upwards, its crust frothing into pumice. The plugs collapsed, releasing with explosive energy the Demon they held captive. From the volcano's throat came a thunderous roar of triumph. Into the air shot a pillar of steam and a cloud of debris. Within an hour it had risen to seventeen miles, more than double the height of Mount Everest, twice as high as any recorded cloud above Mount Vesuvius.

It climbed in a thick column, mushrooming out at its apex, taking the ominous shape of a gigantic pine tree, the classic definition of the first stage of a paroxysmal volcanic outburst.

At 1 p.m. on Sunday, August 26, 1883, a date forever memorable in the long and fearful story of man's struggle with nature, Krakatoa hoisted her battle flag and gave warning that the preliminary sparring was over. The decks were cleared for action. The glove was down in the ring.

Act I of Krakatoa's final paroxysm had begun. It lasted several hours, during which the volcano vomited its stored up magma in a series of explosions until its reservoir was exhausted. Between 1 p.m. and sometime Sunday evening the volcano spewed up its contents in a series of gigantic blasts, which one eyewitness likened to the rhythmic beat of a heavily laden locomotive grinding up a steep gradient, PUFF, *whomph*, *puff, whomph*. Yet, terrible as were Krakatoa's early pulsations, they were only the awesome prelude to its final catastrophic paroxysm.

Hundreds of thousands of people watched or heard Krakatoa's grand opening. Days and weeks later, a handful of stunned survivors told their stories of the catastrophe that struck Java and Sumatra. They were incoherent and confused. No one human being saw the whole disaster. The Straits were blacked out for three days. No mortal eye saw what happened on Krakatoa. The island was engulfed in smoke and flame.

Only years later were geologists able to reconstruct the course of events.

The roar of Krakatoa's opening salvo reverberated across the waters of the Strait. By an odd freak of acoustics, to some listeners the noise was deafening; others hardly heard it. The same disparity of experience described the cloud. Some witnesses remembered it as a towering white pillar; to others it appeared densely black, wide and low. There was considerable disagreement about the weather that Sunday morning. People, all living within an area of one hundred square miles, described it both as fine and sunny and as wet and stormy.

For weeks afterwards survivors argued about the events of the day. According to several the cloud rose high above Krakatoa before they heard the roar. Others heard the noise before they saw the cloud. Both may have been right for light travels faster than sound. Friends and relatives argued about their behaviour. Several people asserted they had experienced a feeling of impending doom and were depressed. On the contrary they had been their ordinary cheerful selves, their companions declared. Controversies developed about how people had behaved under stress. An assistant collector of taxes was ridiculed for sitting on his cash box, amidst flood and flame, refusing to be rescued without his precious guilders, a devotion to duty which cost him his life. A Dutch woman complained she had been shocked and embarrassed by the sight of the controller of her district wandering through the wood stark naked and shameless. The controller, on the other hand, whose clothes had been ripped from him by a whirlwind gust, informed the minister for public instruction and religious education that the lady was not shocked at all. She it was who had no shame, he angrily retorted. The natives of villages lying back of the coast were accused by the Dutch of unhelpfulness and downright antagonism when they implored food and shelter. The Dutch had caused the eruption, the natives retorted; the spirits were retaliating against the Dutch aggression in fighting the Achtinese, a warlike tribe in northern

Sumatra. Like all great calamities, Krakatoa's outburst brought out the best and worst in human nature. It produced no special hero or heroine, no vivid eyewitness historian, no one of the calibre of Young Pliny.

Krakatoa's opening bellow was heard far afield. To one Dutchman the sound was menacing. Three years before, R. D. M. Verbeek had made a geological survey of Krakatoa. The high acidic content of the debris of the 1680 eruption surprised him. In July, 1883, he had been an interested spectator of the volcano's renewed activity. From the decks of the steamer that brought him from a vacation in Holland, Verbeek watched the cloud of steam and ash spouting from two of its little cones. Back home at Buitenzorg, the Dutch mountain resort in the Javanese highlands, Verbeek studied Engineer Schuurman's report of his analysis of Krakatoa's ejecta. It was 65 percent silica, he noticed; approaching the flash point for Indonesian volcanoes. "The explosivity of the Pacific magma increases with its acidity," Verbeek told a friend. When on Sunday, August 26th, he heard low and distant rumbling, the geologist had no doubt whence the sound came, or of its dangerous significance. For some minutes he listened intently, noting the occasional staccato report. Behind him the doors and windows of the house rattled, shaken by the vibrations carried through one hundred miles of air. Verbeek walked to the telegraph office and sent a message to his friend, Dr. Van der Stok, director of the observatory in Batavia, asking for news.

Dr. Van der Stok heard Krakatoa's roar. A precise man, he hurried to the observatory to note the exact time which he recorded in the official diary as 1.06 p.m. From the west came the roll of distant thunder, from nearby the excited buzz of thousands of alarmed Batavians. From the Old Town, a warren of narrow streets and old houses, arose the wailing cry of the Chinese traders. The streets emptied quickly as the frightened Asiatics swarmed to the more open New Town, the Dutch residential district. At 2 p.m. there came a tremendous explosion which was described three days later by the British consul, a Scotsman named H. G. Kennedy, in a letter which was published in the *Scotsman,* as "indescribably awful." The atmosphere, he recalled, became unusually oppressive and the air sluggish. As the afternoon progressed, the reports and bangs grew in strength, and a thunderstorm passed over the city without the inhabitants noticing it. To the Governor-General's enquiry, Anjer answered by telegraph, "Krakatoa vomiting fire and smoke." Dr. Van der Stok passed the information to Verbeek.

The situation in the Straits was far more menacing than in the capital, ninety-four miles distant from the erupting volcano. At the port of Merak, at the narrowest part of the Strait, the work of quarrying stone for the Batavian harbour works was at a standstill. The Sabbath's calm reigned in the camp of the Chinese labourers and in the homes of the Dutch officials which were situated on a low hill behind the town. Early in the day Chief Engineer Nieuwenhys rode off to Batavia to report to his chief, leaving Acting Chief Miner K. A. Naumann in charge. Startled by the sudden roar, Naumann, Works-Accountant E. Peckler, Overseers H. B. Van Diest and J. Kaal, Storekeeper T. S. Townsend, Machinist S. C. Van Essen, and their wives and children rushed from their homes. They saw a vast cloud rise above Krakatoa, forty miles away. Forty-eight hours later when Nieuwenhys struggled back through the devastated countryside, the town of Merak had disappeared and only one of his friends remained alive.

At Anjer, only thirty-one miles across the Strait from Krakatoa, Telegraph Master Schruit sat down to his Sunday dinner with a feeling of satisfaction. The day before he had at last found a dwelling-house to which to bring his wife and children who had been forced to remain in Batavia since his appointment in May. The long separation was nearly over. The house was close to the beach, the view from it fine and extensive. Finishing his dinner Schruit went to the verandah of the hotel from where, on an earlier Sunday, he had watched Krakatoa's opening salvo and had failed to decipher the *Zeeland's* signal. Now, on another Sunday four months later, he watched the ships passing through the Straits. Two he noticed especially, a full-rigged barque beating up against the wind, some twelve miles southeast of Krakatoa, and nearer at hand, a steamer which he recognised as the Government ship, the *Gouveneur General Loudon,* approaching Anjer. His friend, Captain Lindemann, was in a hurry to dock, thought Schruit, noticing the plume of smoke trailing from the steamer's funnel. Schruit's eyes were fixed on the *Loudon* when he heard the roar of Krakatoa's explosion. Looking quickly to his left he saw a column of steam rise above the island. It billowed up, ascending rapidly. To Schruit, it appeared as if thousands of big white balloons had been suddenly released. They rolled upwards, twisting and turning, expanding and bursting. The spectacle was quite different from the one he had witnessed in May. This was something far more serious, he knew instinctively. The surface of the sea was alternately rising and falling. Hurrying to the beach, Schruit met another telegraphist and asked him whether the tide was ebbing or flowing. The man thought it was ebbing, but a sudden rush of water showed that was not the case.

As the two telegraphists watched, the cloud above Krakatoa reached its apex and rolled downwards filling the Straits with dense blackness. Recalling his duty, Schruit groped his way to the telegraph office where his assistant was taking down a message from Batavia asking for news. Schruit ordered him to reply that Krakatoa was in eruption, adding that it was so dark "that one's hand cannot be seen when held before the eyes." He noted the time as 2 p.m. The answer came quickly. Schruit was ordered to keep the telegraph line open until seven o'clock. When he tried to recontact Batavia a few minutes after 2 p.m., the line was dead. Anjer had telegraphed its last message.

Straits-pilot de Vries was on duty at the port office where he was awaiting the *Loudon.* He was in a better position than most to see what was going on, for the building was designed to give an extensive view of the Straits. When he heard the

great roar he swung the port telescope in the direction of
Krakatoa. Through its lens he watched a vast column of steam
rising over the island, and he noticed that it alternated first
black and then white. The strange behaviour of the sea interested him more. It was higher than usual for the time of day,
feverishly agitated, and the water was assuming the colour of
inky blackness. De Vries noticed that his boats were being
driven ashore and he went to save them. Across the water
came rumblings and detonations, accompanied by heavy reports. As he worked, de Vries's attention was drawn to the
Loudon, which was entering the port through the twin prom-
ontories protecting the harbour.

The *Loudon* left Batavia at 8.10 a.m. that morning on a
voyage to Anjer where Captain Lindemann was ordered to
embark 111 coolies and women, and carry them to Telok
Betong, the chief port of the Lampongs, where they were to
be employed on the plantations. The 1,239-ton steamer docked
at Anjer at 2 p.m. Forty-five minutes later, her passengers em-
barked, the *Loudon* sailed for Telok Betong, keeping well to
the east of the erupting island which was casting forth enormous clouds of smoke, passing through a rain of ashes and
small bits of falling stone.

The inky blackness of the sea on that Sunday afternoon also
struck the attention of another resident of Anjer, Mr. Schint.
Weeks later he was interviewed by the Rev. Tennyson-Woods,
who stopped off at Java on his voyage home to England from
Australia, where he sent a long report about the disaster which
was published by the Sydney *Morning Herald.* Schint told the
inquisitive clergyman that every minute the detonations became more violent and finally developed into a sustained roar
that seemed to crush every other sound. As the afternoon
advanced, dense clouds rolled over Anjer, accompanied by
repeated and terrific explosions. The inhabitants showed the
utmost alarm. The Chinese, seizing what valuables they could,
gathered on the beach and tried to secure boats. There was
much confusion. Even the lamps the refugees carried gave

scarcely a glimmer through the falling ash. Neither streets
nor roads could be made out. Only at intervals could voices
be heard above the roar of the explosions.

The crowd on the beach increased. Those who tried to
launch boats found the sea advancing and receding; at one
moment the boats would be left high and dry and at the next
the crowd was swept back by the swelling tide. The water
rose and fell as much as ten feet every quarter hour, smashing
the boats and strewing the beach with wreckage. The panic-
stricken crowd ran from the beach, making for higher ground,
and Schint saw the road strewn with prostrate natives, uttering loud cries and reciting prayers. Some loss of life was caused
by debris falling from the volcano, Schint told Woods.

The Rev. Tennyson-Woods secured another story from an
Englishman, whose name he did not record, a resident in the
village of Chickandie Udik, near Tjaringin. This man told him,
"Everyone was at foot. The reports sounded louder and louder
until the ground shook sensibly. The poor natives thinking
that the end of the world had come, flocked together like sheep,
and made the scene more dismal with their cries and prayers.
Evening set in. The detonations, far from diminishing, increased in violence, startling the people with new crises every
two or three minutes." It had grown dark at 3 p.m., he said.
The roaring of the volcano became louder and louder, and
finally was so heavy that the ground trembled under his feet.
Startling detonations came every two minutes, and the air,
charged with sulphurous fumes, was stifling. From time to
time a deathlike stillness prevailed, broken by further rumbles
and cannon shots.

As the darkness increased and night descended, some cautious coastal dwellers sought safety on the hills behind Anjer.
These heights were the only safe places, but the jungles were
impassable and swarmed with wild beasts, boars, tigers and
pythons. Those who tried to escape along the coastal road
were swept away by the ever rising tides. Drawing on the
combined experience of the survivors, the Rev. Tennyson-
Woods employed his imagination to picture the scene of that

last long night. "In pitchy darkness and sulphurous fumes that were stifling, those who had the shelter of houses remained under cover. Mothers gathered their children around them awaiting the return of light to find some way of escape. During the lingering hours, six very severe shocks of earthquake were felt so that the houses were abandoned. The roaring of the sea became fearful."

Ever mindful of his duty Mr. Schruit set out to trace the break in the telegraph line from Anjer to Batavia, which he knew must be local for he could not even contact Merak seven miles up the coast. He told his story in the Batavia *Handlesblad* a week later:

As soon as possible I went with one of the telegraphists along the line, and ran through the fort, where I was told that a schooner had broken her cable. I proceeded to the landing place which is a canal near the fort, and reached the draw-bridge, the rails of which had already been knocked away. There, a fearful sight met my eyes; a schooner and twenty-five or thirty proas were being carried up and down between the draw-bridge and the ordinary bridge as the water rose and fell, and nothing remained unbroken, including the telegraph wires which had been snapped by the schooner's mast.

But we felt no alarm as the water did not overflow its banks. Not entertaining any idea of danger, I sat down to table at about half-past 8. Of course I had made the necessary arrangements for beginning the repair of the broken line the first thing in the morning.

In the course of the evening, I had frequent occasion to exert my powers of persuasion in an endeavour to reassure several ladies who were greatly alarmed and excited by the surrounding phenomena, and indeed not without reason. Krakatoa began, a little later in the evening, an active eruption; a violent thunderstorm broke over us, and the ground shook and trembled as if "the Day of Judgment" had come.

At half-past 9 the elements had apparently calmed down and a gentle shower of ashes began to fall; the sea was very still so that everyone recovered his usual state of mind. For precaution I went out during the night, or about 1 o'clock in the morning, to the canal to take another look at the damage done, accompanied by the Harbour Master and two neighbours, but we could discover nothing more than the appearance already observed the previous afternoon, viz: the rising and falling of the surface of the sea.

The harbour master whom Schruit mentions was B. F. M. van Leewen. He returned from his visit to the beach to re-assure some of the other Dutch residents of Anjer: Thomas Buijs, the assistant Resident, H. T. van Rosmalen, the supervisor of public works, a widow named Schruit (no relation of the telegraph master), Lighthouse Keeper Schuit, De Jong, a ship's chandler, Registrar Regensburg, the town clerk, and Dr. Dillié.

Further down the coast at Tjaringin the relatives of the native Regent were gathering for a feast. Fifty-seven had been invited and fifty-five turned up. Two nephews made excuses and lived to think themselves very lucky. The Dutch residents of the town gathered to discuss the situation, amongst them Chief of Highways Gaston, assistant Resident John van der Bosch, Chief Telegraphist H. F. Dessauvagies, Works Supervisor P. Schalk, Military Surveyor Hoffman, and the assistant collector of taxes.

At the village of Meeuwenbabi, Lightkeeper M. van Menes carefully noted each stage of the phenomena, entering in his logbook these details:

About	2.30 p.m.	Sky dark in north.
About	6.00 p.m.	Sky dark everywhere, except bright spot S.W.
About	6.10 p.m.	Dry ash falling and pumice fragments.
At	7.00 p.m.	Wind in east.
At	7.30 p.m.	Rain of ash—no pumice.
At	7.50 p.m.	Violent earthquake—everything shook.
At	10.00 p.m.	Heavy weather. Thunder–lightning until 4 a.m.

Along the coast to the west, around Pepper and Welcome bays and on Princess Island, natives and Dutchmen watched and listened to Krakatoa's vomiting and roaring. Beyond Tjaringin the hills ceased and the coast was flanked by a low plain that gave no protection from the rising tides that were lapping the beaches. There was no escaping them. In a dozen villages and hamlets the people spent an anxious night. Before the darkness closed in, several observers noticed the barque, which Schruit had seen earlier, beating up the Strait, dangerously close to the erupting volcano.

The crew of this ship, the British vessel *Charles Bal* registered at Belfast in northern Ireland, on a voyage to Hong Kong, saw Krakatoa's paroxysmal eruption in spectacular close-up. They were nearer to the island than anyone, only ten miles distant, during the night of eruption. Standing in for Java Head on the evening of August 25th, her captain, W. J. Watson, saw thick clouds, flecked with lightning. The vessel passed Princess Island at 9 a.m. on Sunday morning and by noon she was ten miles southwest of Krakatoa with only a small part of the low island showing. An hour later Captain Watson recorded in the ship's log that the islands were covered by a dense black cloud.

Captain Watson did not remark any particular noise and he did not describe the cloud which another ship's captain, forty miles away, likened to a gigantic pine tree and estimated at the low island showing. An hour later Captain Watson recorded for certain events vary considerably with the observations of other eyewitnesses. Watson, in all probability, wrote up his log from memory afterwards, following an experience that could have confused him. On the other hand, he may have forgotten to adjust his chronometer from Indian Ocean time to Indonesian time, an omission which would account for the disparity of exactly one hour in his record.

At 2.30 p.m. Watson noticed some agitation about the point of Krakatoa; "clouds or something being propelled from the north-eastern point with great velocity." From this statement we may deduce that it was the northerly cone of Perboewatan which was then discharging. An hour later, Watson remarked "a strange sound as of a mighty crackling fire, or the discharge of heavy artillery at seconds intervals of time," and at 4.15 p.m. he observed a repetition of the cloud effect "only much more furious and alarming, the matter or whatever it was being propelled with amazing velocity to the north-east." It looked like blinding rain and had the appearance of a furious squall of ashen hue.

Captain Watson at once ordered sail to be shortened to top-sails and foresail. The *Charles Bal* was in a fearful situation, within ten miles of an erupting volcano, as her log record shows:

At five the roaring noise continued and increased; wind moderate from south-south-west; darkness spread over the sky, and a hail of pumice-stone fell on us, many pieces being of considerable size and quite warm. Had to cover up the skylights, to save the glass, while feet and head had to be protected with boots and southwesters. About six o'clock the fall of larger stones ceased, but there continued a steady fall of a smaller kind, most blinding to the eyes, and covering the decks to three or four inches very speedily, while an intense blackness covered the sky and land and sea. Sailed on our course until we got what we thought was a sight of Fourth Point Light (close to Anjer), then brought ship to the wind, south-west, as we could not see any distance, and we knew not what might be in the Straits, the night being a fearful one. The blinding fall of sand and stones, the intense blackness above and around us, broken only by the incessant glare of varied kinds of lightning and the continued explosive roars of Krakatoa, made our situation a truly awful one. At 11 p.m., having stood off from the Java shore, wind strong from the south-west, the island, west-north-west, eleven miles distant, became more visible, chains of fire appearing to ascend and descend between the sky and it, while on the south-west end there seemed to be a continued roll of balls of white fire; the wind, though strong, was hot and choking, sulphurous, with a smell as of burning cinders, some of the pieces falling on us being like iron cinders, and the lead from the bottom of thirty fathoms came up quite warm.

Twenty miles behind the *Charles Bal* lay the German ship *Berbice*, commanded by Captain William Logan of Greenock. She came from New York and was on a voyage to Batavia. When he entered the western end of the Straits on August 26th, Logan, seeing darkness and flashes of light ahead, thought a tropical storm was brewing. The sky looked threatening and the sun was burning hot. He shortened sail and kept on his course until six o'clock, when it became suddenly dark and the vessel ran into a shower of ashes. Clearly a volcano was in eruption. Thinking of his cargo, which was petroleum, Logan deemed it prudent to lie to for the night, in the centre of the Straits, midway between Vlakke Hoek and Princess Island, a position he did not leave for a week. In addition to the valuable cargo of oil, the *Berbice* carried a small and apparently insignificant package. It had been entrusted to Captain Logan at New York with the injunction to get it as quickly as possible to Java where it was destined for the botanical gardens at Buitenzorg. The package contained, he was told, five rubber trees from Brazil.

These five little trees, carried in a ship's hold through the devastation wrought by Krakatoa, brought incalculable wealth to the East Indies. Two of them still flourish in the gardens at Buitenzorg where they are pointed out as the progenitors of a great and flourishing industry.

Captain Logan had little time or inclination to think of his strange cargo that night. His log records:

> Midnight—The ash shower is becoming heavier and is intermixed with fragments of pumice stone. The lightning and thunder became worse and worse. Lightning flashes shot past around the ship. Fireballs continually fell on deck and burst into sparks. We saw flashes of light falling quite close to us on the ship, heard fearful rumbles and explosions, sometimes upon the deck and sometimes among the rigging. The man at the rudder

received heavy shocks on one arm. The copper sheathing of the
rudder became glowing hot from the electric discharges. The
fiery phenomena on board the ship manifested themselves at
every moment. Now and then when any sailor complained that
he had been struck, I did my best to set his mind at ease, and
endeavoured to talk the idea out of him until I myself, holding
fast at the time to some ropes in the rigging with one hand and
bending my head out of reach of the blinding ash shower which
swept past my face, had to let go my hold owing to a severe
shock in the arm, upon which I was unable to move for several
minutes afterwards. I now had sails laid over the hatches for fear
lest the fire around should set my cargo ablaze. I also directed
the rudder to be securely fastened, ordered all the men below,
and remained on deck with only Morland the mate.

At the same time, Captain Watson of the *Charles Bal* was
describing the sky as "one second intense blackness, the next
a blaze of fire." Heavy waves were battering the Javanese
coast, one storming sea sweeping away the Chinese camp at
Merak.

A hundred miles to the west, the *Bay of Naples*, Captain
Tidmarsh, ninety-six days out from Penarth, South Wales, on
a voyage to Singapore, encountered a bank of ash and falling
pumice. Captain Tidmarsh decided to delay his transit of the
Straits. Twenty-four days elapsed before he was able to get
through to Batavia.

Across the Straits on the Sumatra coast at Kalimbang, Controller and Mrs. Beyerinck were due that Sunday morning to
attend the opening of a new market at the village of Tjanti, a
well-to-do campong. A small buffalo was to be slaughtered,
the gamlan orchestra would play and there would be much
dancing and gambling. Mrs. Beyerinck did not want to go.
She was worried. Cholera was rampant and the victims were
mounting. One of her maids had died. The girl had done the
children's washing. For several days Mrs. Beyerinck had felt
that something dreadful was going to happen. Birds, she knew,
always left a place where a calamity was to befall, and they
had been restless for days, flying round in flocks, settling in

trees, making loud noises and taking off again in wide sweeps. It was an ominous sign, agreed the ayah. The controller tried to calm his young wife's fears. The natives were highly superstitious, he pointed out. The opening of a market would be a joyous occasion. It would cheer her up. He persuaded his wife to accompany him and they set off by carriage. Mrs. Beyerinck did not enjoy herself and she kept pressing her husband to return home. Finally he agreed and by 1 p.m. the carriage was bowling along the coast road.

It is difficult to discern from Mrs. Beyerinck's long and agonised story what she and her husband saw and heard at that time. They were less than twenty-four miles from the point of eruption, closer than anyone except Captain Watson of the *Charles Bal.* Mrs. Beyerinck says she heard a distinct noise and noticed that Krakatoa was no longer visible, being surrounded by pitch-black clouds through which the sun looked blood red and its rays reddish. She does not remark on the size or shape of the cloud or the intensity of the explosions which others observed so accurately. Between 1 p.m. on August 26th and September 1st when she and her husband were rescued, Mrs. Beyerinck underwent an experience that almost unhinged her mind. Her actions on reaching home that day bespeak her fears; what she saw and heard must have frightened her nearly out of her wits.

Upon reaching her house, which stood on a slight eminence overlooking the beach, Mrs. Beyerinck tried to persuade her husband to flee at once to Amboel Balik, a village high on the slopes of Radjah Bassa, where they owned a small hut. He would not hear of leaving Kalimbang. "If we flee now," the controller told his wife, "the natives will be overcome with anxiety and disorders may break out." Many of the savage natives of the interior were in Kalimbang for the pepper-crop picking. "We will wait until the emergency is greater," he announced. "It may then be too late," cried Mrs. Beyerinck, hugging her fourteen-months' old son, whom she was still feeding. "Now, now, all in good time. You look as white as a ghost and that is not good for the child," replied the controller.

Mr. Beyerinck went to his office and Mrs. Beyerinck stayed
with the children. She sat indoors all afternoon, and she makes
no remark of what she saw and heard, except that a gamlan
orchestra was playing somewhere in the town and the toll of
the great Rabana drum sounded like a death knell.

Controller Beyerinck went to the beach where he saw the
Loudon steaming up the coast on her voyage to Telok Betong,
and he watched heavy waves throwing native proas on shore,
where they were dashed to pieces. The highest waves reached
the outbuildings of his own house. By 8 p.m. Mr. Beyerinck's
mind was made up. He sent his clerk, Mr. Tojaka, to his wife
with the message to prepare herself and the children for immediate flight. The children were to be warmly dressed, and
she was to give them a good meal. Mrs. Beyerinck had got the
children dressed sometime before the message came, but she
herself was still wearing a sarong. In her story, which was
published in several Javanese newspapers, Mrs. Beyerinck described the last wretched evening she spent at her home, surrounded by her faithful servants.

> If I shut my eyes, I see it all before me, the pieces of chicken,
> the rice and my faithful young Radjah exhorting me to eat. "You
> must eat, Madam, for you don't know what is going to happen.
> Come now, take a little rice." He served some up but I could not
> get it down. It was as if my throat was sealed. I went to the front
> balcony. The pumice had been falling for hours but in pieces no
> bigger than peas. Then I saw someone coming up the garden
> with a lantern. It was Jeroemoeidi (one of her servants), who
> said to me in a very worried manner "The *Antoe Laoet* (the Sea
> Ghost) is close by. The sea has gone. Far, far away I hear the
> waves." "How can it have gone? Perhaps it is at low ebb?" I
> asked. "Come and see. It should now be high tide. It is a worry-
> ing sight, for all the coral reefs along the coast, which at the
> lowest ebb lie a fathom below the surface and which I can sail
> over in my sloop, are now dried out." A whole lot of natives now
> came up to the house and corroborated Jeroemoeidi's story.
>
> My eldest boy was playing with the ayah on the sofa. My
> eldest girl was standing in the bedroom. I was lying on the bed

and the maid was standing near me. I was feeding my youngest son. Then I heard, above the noise of the pumice falling on the roof, above the thunder from the mountain. a frightful roaring which approached at lightning speed. My hair stood on end. I leapt up clutching my youngest child and shouted, "Come here, come here, everyone together." The wave reached the house but it didn't go further than the back yard. It destroyed the office and surrounding outhouses, and my husband and Mr. Tojaka were only just able to escape with their lives by climbing up a cocoa-nut tree after they had fled from the office. As soon as the wave receded my husband dashed to the house, but he could not get upstairs as the stairs had been washed away. He shouted, "Wife, wife, come downstairs quickly, just jump and I'll catch you," and to the servant he called, "Turn the horses and animals loose."

It must have been about 8.30 p.m. when the Beyerinck family began their flight into the interior, an experience Mrs. Beyerinck hoped she would never have to go through again. They did not dare take the coastal road and they were forced to walk through an extensive paddy field full of water, and then through a wood in which there was no path. They sank into mud at every step. Sometimes it reached Mrs. Beyerinck's knees. Behind came a terrible roaring, as if the sea was trying to catch them. When Mrs. Beyerinck tried to say something to Mr. Tojaka, who was helping her along, she found she could not speak. She tried to make a noise. It felt as though her throat was dried out and someone was trying to cut her tonsils with a knife. She felt her neck. To her horror it was covered with leeches. When they reached the wood, the party lost their way. A crowd of natives came fleeing in their direction. One of them led the way, the Beyerincks following, holding on to one another. They reached their hut at midnight. Mrs. Beyerinck laid the exhausted children on the bed and opened the box of provisions which yielded some seltzer water and a bottle of orange syrup. The family settled down in the tiny room which had two windows covered by bamboo slats. Mrs. Beyerinck thanked God they had at last reached safety. No one could sleep, for the noises coming from Krakatoa were quite ghastly. Around the hut lay thousands of terrified natives, moaning and crying and praying to Allah for deliverance.

The *Loudon* reached Telok Betong at the head of Lampong Bay at 7.30 p.m. During the 65-mile voyage from Anjer, Captain Lindemann noticed that "the island of Krakatoa was casting forth enormous columns of smoke," but he makes no remark of the waves and tides which observers on shore noticed. It is one of the curious oddities of Krakatoa's outburst that the ships navigating the Straits were little affected by these waves which grew in intensity as the eruption progressed. Nevertheless, Captain Lindemann, when he dropped anchor in the roadstead, realised that something was amiss. The current in the bay was unusually strong and a number of native proas lay smashed on the beach. The jetty had been washed away, and he saw the harbour master gesticulating from the shore. Lindemann decided it was too rough to launch a boat. Reports made subsequently by the Resident, N. Altheers, and his assistant, J. F. Wynveldt, explain what had happened. Following a particularly heavy discharge from Krakatoa at 4 p.m., high waves flooded the beach. Strollers and the harbour master, who was awaiting the *Loudon,* were driven from the jetty which was carried away at 6 p.m. The inundation of the low-lying shore led to a general flight to higher ground, several people venturing back to collect their possessions. They were quickly driven away from the town by the waves which mounted higher and higher, the flood reaching within 30 feet of the Residency which was built on a hill 122 feet high. At 6.30 p.m., Mr. Altheers noticed that the sky was copper coloured in Krakatoa's direction and light ash was falling. Another European resident of Telok Betong, whose name we do not know, and who told his story in the Java *Bode* on September 19th, went to the shore to assist the natives whose houses had been submerged.

The Dutch barque *Marie,* 570 tons, engaged in the salt trade, was torn from her moorings in the roadstead. She had reached Telok Betong the night before, and on Sunday morning her first mate, M. P. Stokhluysen, began a letter to his family in Holland, one which he did not finish for several days. The morning, he told his mother, was fine but the sky became overcast and he heard loud rumblings in the distance. During the afternoon a strong tide set into the bay and the little ship was twisted and tossed, turning round and round like a top. The tide receded, leaving the beach open and the fish were left stranded. The tide came back, the waves crashing several proas into the *Marie,* and from them he and his men rescued ten natives.

Several anonymous reporters described their experiences at Telok Betong, forty miles from Krakatoa. One of them, who seems to have been the harbour master, said that, while he was awaiting the *Loudon,* he was nearly swept away by the sea rising high. The furious waves struck him down eight times but he had enough strength left to struggle out of the water. Another survivor stated that about 6 p.m. the sea rose unusually high and rushed up the shore, the rollers becoming larger and larger.

That night, says Captain Lindemann of the *Loudon,* "The lightning struck the main mast conductor five or six times," and "the mud-rain which covered the masts, rigging and decks was phosphorescent and on the rigging presented the appearance of St. Elmo's fire. The native crew engaged themselves busily in putting this phosphorescent light out with their hands, and were so intent on this occupation that the stokers left the engine rooms for the purpose, so that the European engineers were left to drive the machinery for themselves. The natives pleaded that if this phosphorescent light, or any portion of it, found its way below, a hole would be burnt in the ship; not that they feared the ship taking fire, but they thought the light was the work of evil spirits, and that if the ill-omen light found its way below, the evil spirits would triumph in their design to scuttle the ship."

Anchored near the jetty lay the Dutch gunboat *Berouw.* Next day the vessel suffered a catastrophe which must be unique in the annals of volcanic disaster.

As the Sunday evening progressed, the people of Telok

Betong heard explosions like an artillery barrage. A heavy
wind blew, ash fell, and by 10.30 a.m. the town was engulfed
in total darkness. Everyone was frozen with horror. Ten convicts working in a chain gang at the lighthouse lay on the
ground trembling, their manacles clinking and rattling. The
lightkeeper refused to allow the guard to take them inland.

The experiences of people living on the shores of Semanka
Bay were similar to those in Lampong Bay, except that, being
slightly further from Krakatoa, the early manifestations of the
eruption were less dramatic. The first big wave reached Pajoeng at the head of the bay between 5 and 6 p.m. Controller
Le Soeur heard sounds like cannon shots. He was lying reading
on a long chair at the back of his house. Knowing that the
Resident had gone to Beneawang, he decided to investigate
and he went to the beach, taking the heads of his department
with him. On arriving at the shore they could see nothing unusual and returned home. Scarcely had Le Soeur sat down and
reopened his book when a servant reported that the sea was
rising and part of the village was flooded. He went back to
the beach. The villagers were in their houses, wailing and
calling, "*Allah il Allah.*" He restored order and commanded
the women and children to leave their houses. As he watched,
the sea receded and the flood subsided. A rain of ash began to
fall. Le Soeur remained in the village all night.

The story of that Sunday night all round the northern
shores of the Strait was similar. Black clouds were seen rising
from Krakatoa, explosions were heard and waves battered the
beaches. Low ground was flooded, boats were smashed and
houses were demolished. Many people fled inland. At Benkolen, Lightkeeper F. Hamwyck ordered the convicts who
were repairing the installation at the lighthouse to remain. At
Kroe, Controller Dr. H. W. Horst, a scientifically minded man,
decided to keep an exact record of the phenomena. On Noordwatcher Island, on Sumatra's eastern shore, outside the Straits,
Lightkeeper H. van der Meulen noticed several ships beating
about, trying to enter the Straits.

The American barque *W. H. Besse,* sailing from Manila to

Boston by way of the Indian and Atlantic oceans, Captain Baker commanding, came down the eastern coast of Sumatra, her first officer noting in the logbook:

Sunday, August 26th, 1883.
 The day commenced with strong breezes and thick cloudy weather; at 4 a.m. hove short; at 6 a.m. got under weigh, wind S.W. At 4 p.m., wind hauling ahead, came to anchor; the sky at this time having a threatening appearance; atmosphere very close and smoky. At 5 p.m. heard a quick succession of heavy reports sounding like the broadside of a man-of-war, only far louder and heavier; heard these reports at intervals throughout the night; the sky was intensely dark, the wind having a dull moaning; through the rigging also noticed a light fall of ashes.

Captain Baker decided to anchor. He suspected that Krakatoa might be in eruption. The *W. H. Besse* had been in Batavia since June 24th, undergoing repairs after running aground, and he had heard about the volcano's renewed activity. He preferred to remain at the safe distance of seventy-five miles. The Norwegian barque *Borjild*, Captain Amundsen, came to rest close to the *W. H. Besse*. Nearer the Sumatra shore, the British ships, *Sir Robert Sale* and *Norham Castle*, lay hoved to. Captain Woolbridge, of the *Sir Robert Sale*, relates that at one period the cloud above the mountain "presented the appearance of an immense pine tree, with the stem and branches formed with volcanic lightning." And at another phase, he says, "It looked like a titanic wall with bursts of fork lightning, at times like large serpents rushing through the air." After sunset it resembled a "blood-red curtain, with the edges of all shades of yellow." Captain O. Sampson of the *Norham Castle* states that Krakatoa appeared to be alight with flickering flames rising behind a dense black cloud; at times balls of fire rested on his ship's mastheads and the extremities of the yardarms.
 Several other ships lay further out. Captain Thompson of the *Medea*, then sailing at a point seventy-six miles east-northeast of Krakatoa, observed a black smoky mass rolling in great billows up into the heavens to an altitude which he estimated

at not less than seventeen miles. He heard heavy explosions, each followed by clouds of dust, and he noted their recurrence every ten minutes.

On Sunday while approaching the Straits, Captain Strachan of the steamer *Anerley* thought he heard a noise like that of distant cannonading, and it soon attracted the attention of all on board; flashes of light were seen to the southwestward. In the evening an arch of light rose in a short time from the horizon to the zenith. Three aneroid barometers on board rose and fell nearly an inch at short intervals.

Closest to Krakatoa of all the ships gathering at the eastern entrance to the Straits was the *Hope,* commanded by Captain Davies. On board, Seaman Dalby noted that everything seemed as usual that morning. The vessel lay close to St. Nicholas Point and the crew were occupied in discharging the cargo of rice into lighters alongside. About 1 p.m. Dalby was startled by loud rumblings which he thought at first came from beneath the ship.

At Batavia the astronomical clock in the observatory stopped at 11.32.18 seconds that Sunday night. Otherwise the day passed without any remarkable incident. The citizens of the capital were disturbed and uneasy. Telegraphic communication with Anjer had been lost since shortly after 2 p.m. No one knew what was happening in the Straits, and fears were expressed for relatives and friends. That night there was a strong smell of sulphur in the air and many detonations were heard. At intervals there were strange silences that made people more nervous than the bangs and roars. Domestic animals were equally alarmed, forcing their way into houses, crying and cackling.

It was already pitch dark when night fell with tropical suddenness over the Straits of Sunda. The Chinese camp at Merak was in ruins. The showers of pumice and stones were so heavy that the Dutch officials did not dare venture to investigate without carrying umbrellas to protect their heads. Heavy waves were pounding the shores at Anjer and Tjaringin, and across the Straits in Lampong and Semanka bays the roar from Krakatoa was almost continuous. Every few minutes the volcano belched out tons of pumice and ash which rained down on sea and land.

During the afternoon and early evening of Sunday, Krakatoa vomited out the gas-charged magma rising to the surface from the depths below. This was ejected in a series of *whomphs,* each accompanied by the roar of explosion. Thousands of tons of debris and pumice were thrown into the air, some pieces as large as locomotives, others as small as beads. Each explosion was followed by a moment of silence as fresh magma surged up the chimney.

On the shores of the Sunda Strait that night hardly anyone went to bed. No one slept. Crouched in their homes or hiding in woods, the people watched Krakatoa in all its terrifying glory. Every few minutes there came a burst of brilliance. One moment every detail of the landscape stood out starkly. The next second it was blacker than the blackest night, recalled more than one eyewitness.

6. Long Night

FROM JAVA and Sumatra rose a great cry of fear. The distraught people turned to their gods for aid. *"Allah il Allah,"* prayed the Moslems. "Lord, deliver us," beseeched the Christians. Krakatoa's mighty roars drowned out their puny cries.

As midnight struck, Krakatoa passed from its opening to its final stage of paroxysmal eruption. The red-hot magma surging up the chimney from the reservoir below was becoming exhausted. Above the level of the freshly rising magma a void formed. The roof of the chamber, its supports withdrawn, sagged and caved. Rocks fell; more followed. Full collapse was only a matter of time. The crack of doom was but a step away.

The terrified people who were experiencing the volcano's spectacular display did not know what was happening. Krakatoa was enveloped in dense cloud, lit by flames and lurid glow. The Straits were blacked out. The roar of eruption deafened. Hot pumice and ash raised down. The sea rose and fell. Waves pounded beaches and flooded low ground. They receded only to return, climbing higher and higher, catching the unwary and the foolhardy. On Monday came disaster, dire and utter.

At 1 a.m. the village of Sirik, six miles south of Anjer, was submerged by a big wave that swept in from the sea. Few of its inhabitants had fled and many were drowned. The headmen escaped to Anjer where no wave is reported at that time. The waves were curiously local and discriminating. They struck some places and avoided others close by. When certain towns and villages were destroyed is unknown; many were submerged several times.

Agitated, yet excited, Verbeek prowled his garden at Buitenzorg, one hundred miles from Krakatoa. Three weeks later the Governor-General of the Dutch East Indies ordered him to investigate the eruption. Verbeek made several visits to the island and two years later he published his detailed report. At this distance of time it is permissible to credit him with some foreknowledge of what was taking place and allow him to paint an imaginary picture of the scene which no human eye beheld.

Verbeek knew the disaster area, and he might have told us, if we had been standing beside him, that the danger was increasing. How much he may have foreseen is conjectural, but drawing upon his later conclusions it is possible that he might have forecast the engulfment of Krakatoa's three cones, their entire collapse, resulting in the formation of a subterranean caldera, into which the sea poured and from which it was ejected with explosive violence. From the frothing whirlpool gushed out a wave of gigantic size and shape, a wall of water which made the little waves that crept up the coast earlier that day seem puny by comparison. Krakatoa's "Big Bang and Great Wave" are as yet only figments of Verbeek's imagination. The coastal dwellers and the seamen navigating or approaching the Straits had still some hours of comparative respite.

As the ship's bell struck midnight, the *Charles Bal* groped past Princess Island, its headland looming from the Javanese shoreline. Anjer, the vessel's first port of call, lay ahead. Out in the channel, ten miles distant, Krakatoa roared and shook. The barque sailed on, making slow progress in the thick darkness and turgid seas. Captain Watson noted in his log that from midnight to 4 a.m. the wind was strong, though unsteady, coming from between south-southwest and west-southwest. One second the sky was intensely black, the next a blaze of fire. Over the vessel's mastheads and yardarms danced pink flames. Pumice rained on the decks and the whole ship was covered with ash.

Behind and out of sight of the *Charles Bal*, the *Berbice* rode out the storm. At midnight her captain wrote in the vessel's log: "Ashes increased, pieces of pumice-stone, thunder and lightning increased, fire balls fell on deck and were scattered about, fearful roaring, copper at the helm got hot; helmsman, captain, and several sailors were struck by electric discharges; sail over hatches to prevent fire, helm tied, crew sent below, captain and master kept guard. At 2 a.m. the ashes, three feet thick, were lying on the ship. I had continually to pull my legs out of the ashy layers to prevent them from being buried therein. I now called all hands on deck, with lanterns, to clear away the ashes, though the weather was unchanged, and the fearful electric phenomena, explosions, and rumbles still continued. The ashes were hot, though not perceived to be so at the moment of their falling on the skin. They burned large holes in our clothing and in the sails. At eight o'clock in the morning there was no change. At that hour it was still quite dark, and the ash showers were becoming heavier."

The coastal dwellers did not consult their clocks and watches that morning. It is difficult to discern, therefore, when certain events occurred. The reports are spasmodic and uncertain.

Krakatoa's Grand Collapse began at 4.40 a.m., it was agreed afterwards. It was followed by a loud explosion and a big wave. They affected people differently. The anonymous Englishman, living at Chickandie Udik, describes the scene he witnessed:

At half-past four, the reports sounded distant but gradually they became louder, and finally so heavy that the ground trembled under our feet. Everyone was afoot. The poor superstitious natives, thinking that the end of the world had come, flocked together like sheep and made the scene still more dismal by their continuous loud praying. The dull, thundering sounds continued, and far from decreasing in violence, they increased in strength. Sleep was impossible, from detonations startling people every two or three minutes. The air, charged with sulphurous fumes, was stifling. Thick clouds darkened the sky. A greyish streak was seen on the horizon. Day broke, but the sun was not visible. The rumble had ceased and a death-like calm prevailed around. Everything, however, looked strange. One hour, two hours passed without the light becoming brighter. At half-past seven, the light even diminished, and at 8 o'clock it became impossible to read without lamp light. A death-like stillness prevailed, only broken by the dull rumble. In the distance an unsteady light could be distinguished, apparently coming from the crater of Krakatoa. Thus the dreadful night drew to an end.

Two residents of Anjer, the Lloyd's agent who was named Schuit, and another man called Schint, who must not be confused with Schruit, the telegraph master, had no apprehensions for the safety of the town at 2 a.m. Both men decided to await the coming of dawn before going to the beach to inspect the scene. Schuit remained in his house, comforting his family who numbered seven relatives. Mr. Schruit, the telegraph master, exhausted by his efforts to trace the broken cable, was resting at the hotel when he heard a shattering explosion which he timed at 4.45 a.m. He went at once to the bridge where the line-watcher and the telegraphist were busy repairing the cable.

The first great wave took just over thirty minutes to cross the water to Anjer. It struck the town at 6.30 a.m., reaching a height of thirty-three feet, looking like a "wall of water" to one terrified spectator.

Schruit tells the story of his experiences at the bridge:

I there met some of the towns-people; amongst others Nevianus Schmit, who, after hearing my account of what had happened, kindly offered to fetch me a cup of tea. Whilst I was expecting this friendly mark of attention, I happened to look up and perceived an enormous wave in the distance looking like a mountain rushing onwards, followed by two others that seemed still greater. I stood for an instant on the bridge horrified at the sight, but had sufficient presence of mind to warn the telegraphist and line-watcher of the danger, and then ran as fast as my legs could carry me. The roaring wave followed as fast, knocking to atoms everything that came in its way.

Never have I run so fast in my life, for, in the most literal sense of the word, death was at my heels; and it was the thought of my wife and our children, who would be left destitute by my losing my life, that gave me superhuman strength. The flood-

wave was hardly thirty paces from me. It had destroyed the
draw-bridge, the hotel, the house of the Assistant Resident, in
short everything that it struck.

At last I fell utterly exhausted with my race against death, on
rising ground, and saw to my amazement the wave retreating.
I gasped for breath, but a hearty offering of thanks to Heaven
rose through my choking throat for my deliverance and for the
Providential care by which my family had been left in Batavia.
Had they been at Anjer, there would have been no chance of
safety, for I should at the first sight of the danger have hastened to their assistance, in which case we must all have been
drowned.

Schuit, the Lloyd's agent, had gone to the beach to see about
the mooring of his boats. While engaged in this work an immense wave, the height of which he estimated at ninety feet,
swept without the slightest warning over Anjer, completely
ruining the place and penetrating inland to the distance of
two miles. Schuit saved his life by jumping into one of his
boats, which was close at hand. Seven of his family were
amongst the victims of this flood. The few survivors made their
way as best they could inland, but, to add to the horrors of
the scene, the atmosphere grew pitch dark, and boiling mud
fell in showers.

Pilot de Vries told his escape story in greater detail:

As usual I rose early in the morning and went out into the
open air; it was then fine weather. I proceeded towards the beach
to look after my boats and found one of them a little out of
order upon which I determined to put the craft to rights as soon
as possible. In my walk home, it must have been about 6 o'clock,
on seeing Captain de Jong, an old gentleman well-known at
Anjer standing in front of his house, I entered into conversation
with him on the weather and other unimportant topics. After a
few minutes had elapsed, I suddenly heard in the direction of
the beach the cry "banjir datang" (a flood is coming) and, turning round, I saw in the distance, an immense, enormous black-
looking mass of water, appearing at first sight mountain high,
rush on with a fearful roar and lightning-like rapidity. At the

next moment the water uplifted and overflowed me with such force that it knocked me over and I performed several tumbles on my head as skilfully as the best acrobat.

Swept onwards between air and water with frightful swiftness by this black flood carrying along with it articles of every kind, I luckily kept all my wits about me, and became firmly convinced that often as I had been nigh at Death's door I this time could not escape him. I commended my soul to God and hoped no longer. At that moment for one instant I was borne aloft by the wave. I could then breathe, my head being above water. On the surface of the boundless expanse of waters I was carried along like a straw, and a great variety of articles, including much furniture, drifted past me with horrifying swiftness. I was dashed against a cocoanut tree which I endeavoured to grasp, but the current was too strong for me. At the next moment I was more fortunate with another tree. I got a firm hold of it and clung closely to its trunk which, though it bowed and quivered from the fearful impulse of the water, offered me support and might ensure my safety. As well as I could I climbed up it several feet, but the flood seemed to be steadily rising, at least my legs were still in the water. Suddenly the large attap roof of a house on bamboo posts came floating towards where my tree stood, and striking upon the same, jammed one leg so tightly against it that I almost cried out with pain.

Seeing myself threatened on all sides by death and perceiving safety nowhere, not even in my place of refuge, I thought for a moment of letting go my hold and dying. I suffered fearfully and felt my leg jammed between the tree and the roof, becoming crushed. How long I remained in this state is unknown to me. Perhaps only a few minutes, but these minutes passed in dread of death seemed to lengthen into hours. Suddenly I felt relief. Probably either from the direction of the current changing or from a whirlpool forming or from some other cause, the bamboo roof swung to one side and freed my leg from the fearful squeezing. I had still the strength and the will to climb a couple of feet higher so as to avoid being jammed a second time, and thus take advantage of any chance of safety available under the circumstances.

I looked round. A fearful sight met my eyes. Where Anjer stood I saw nothing but a foaming and furiously rushing flood above the surface of which only a couple of trees and the tops of roofs were visible. In my neighbourhood stood the house of the old gentleman, Mr. de Jong. He and his wife had taken refuge on the flat roof of their house which happened to be not yet overflowed. These old people were, like me, in deadly peril, and walked restlessly along the sides of the roof, doubtless counting the seconds which separated them from death. They were the only living beings I could see. At a given moment, however, the water fell with great rapidity, and flowed back into the sea; I saw it ebb away from under my feet and soon became aware that I could now safely slide down from my high place of refuge and seek safe shelter elsewhere.

And I did so. I again stood on firm ground. But what a sight met my half-stupefied gaze. It was a scene of the utmost confusion which no pen can describe. Immense quantities of broken furniture, beams, pieces of wood, trees, broken vessels, human corpses, all these formed a wildly confused mass heaped together in all directions. I crept on hands and feet over many recognisable articles, stumbled from time to time upon corpses jammed among furniture, and had at last the good fortune to reach higher ground in the neighbourhood of the Chinese quarter. On seeing a horror-struck Chinaman standing in front of his shop, I begged him to give me a glass of water but he could not supply me with any, upon which he hastened inside and handed me a bottle of cognac. I was upon the point of fainting, but I put the bottle to my lips and took a deep draught of the strengthening and inspiriting fluid.

Meanwhile having recovered a little, I looked once more from the place on which I stood towards the spot where I had dwelt. My house had disappeared, naturally with every article of my property that happened to be therein. I was thus bereft of roof, clothing, money, and in short of everything. I was poorer than the poorest, for my only possessions were what I stood in, and even the latter were partly in tatters and scarcely covered my wounded limbs.

Hence there was nothing more to hope for from Anjer, and as I deemed myself the only survivor from the calamity which had destroyed the whole of that town, I decided as soon as possible to leave this scene of horror and hasten to Serang in order to bring word of the event thither. In the church-yard I saw Mr. de Jong and his wife who had dragged themselves there. I afterwards heard that having fainted there, they disappeared in the second tidal wave.

Meanwhile a terrific ash shower had begun to fall. As quickly as my wounded feet would allow me I stepped on along a road strewn with obstructions of all kinds, and had walked several miles when I came in sight of the post cart bound to Serang; the horse drawing it was making fruitless efforts to get through the layer of soft lukewarm ashes that overspread the road everywhere. The animal could hardly get along step by step, hence I overtook the cart with the utmost ease; though it, however, afforded me no protection against the furious ash showers. How I was enabled to find the strength to accomplish, besides the whole distance between Anjer and Serang without succumbing and dying of fatigue on the road, is incomprehensible to me. Assuredly a higher power has supported me. Moreover, the desire of self-preservation always urged me on when my strength was on the point of failing me.

Another Anjer resident had a no less remarkable escape. Dr. Dillié was lying on his bed when the wave struck. He was washed from the bed and jammed amongst the furniture, amidst swirling water that tossed him through the window. He picked himself up and struggled through the flood to the kitchen where he found his wife, her sister and his child standing on the fireplace. Collecting his family, Dr. Dillié fled towards the mountains, defying the heavy showers of ashes and screening the child as best he could. As they ran, the refugees noticed that in all Anjer not one stone of the houses stood upon another. After wandering for some hours they reached a village, but the people there would not allow them to rest. Chased away, unable to get a mouthful of rice or a draught of water, notwithstanding every entreaty, the doctor and his family sought a quiet place on which to lie undisturbed. At length, in the indignant words of the Dutch newspaper reporter who recorded the story, "One native, more compassionate than the others, deigned to point out to these Christian dogs a forsaken village where they could get some rice and pieces of fish. One lady, by her entreaties and in exchange for two gold rings, obtained a glass of foul muddy water and deemed herself and her family fortunate in getting this refreshment."

Several other survivors described their escapes in the local newspapers. One said, "I went out about 5.15. After having talked with several persons, I saw the wave still far off, rapidly making way towards us. I ran away, was followed by the wave, fell down quite exhausted but happily on a hill, where the water could not reach me. Before my eyes all the houses along the beach were destroyed." Another reported: "I was early at the beach [early, after Indian habit, might be at 5 o'clock]. When I returned home I heard a cry, 'The flood comes.' On looking round I saw a high wave which I could not escape; I was lifted from the ground, but caught hold of a tree. Then I perceived several waves which followed the first; the place where Anjer had been before was covered by a turbulent sea, upon which some trees and roofs of houses were still peeping out. After the wave had flowed back I left the tree and found myself in the midst of the devastation." A third person, who was still in bed at six o'clock, was lifted up by the wave and deposited on a hill, still lying on his bed.

The numbers of those swept off by the wave at Anjer cannot be given even approximately, the scenes which occurred there being described as heart-rending. Children saw their parents perish before their eyes, and wives their husbands. The wife of the assistant Resident, Madame Buijs, when standing in the back gallery of her house with her child, was swept into a bathroom by the wave which flung her repeatedly against the sides. On being again carried away and borne out by the raging water, she saw her husband struggling to reach a tree, against which he was shortly afterwards dashed to death. This unfortunate lady was thereupon cast upon a hillock where her child also soon died, and she thereupon fainted from exhaustion, the result of exertion, fatigue and loss of blood from the wounds she received. Only sixteen of the European residents of Anjer were saved.

Mr. Schruit ran to Kares, a village two and one-half miles

from Anjer, where he was out of danger. As soon as he had recovered his breath he obtained writing materials from the headman and wrote a report to the chief inspector of tele-graphs and to the Resident of Bantam, which he sent off by messenger. Having done his duty Schruit returned towards Anjer to save anything he could. "But I had hardly got outside the house when I perceived a lady rushing towards me with frightful anxiety and almost without clothes. This was Madame Schuit, the poor lady who had had the misfortune to lose her two children, and who had been obliged to leave her husband in the next village with his spine injured, to hasten for assist-ance. We offered all the help we could and borrowed for the sorely tried woman a sarong and a kabaya [articles of native clothing]. And we requested the assistant headman to have a litter prepared so that we might go in search of Mr. Schuit."

The waterworks overseer at Anjer was drowned when fleeing with his family, and along with him the little fortune of the family, about 20,000 guilders, disappeared. His widow was left completely destitute.

The fourteen Europeans who died at Anjer were listed as Thomas W. Buijs, assistant Resident, and his child who died in his mother's arms during the flight, B. F. M. van Leewen, the harbour master, H. T. van Rosmalen, supervisor, Civilian Public Works, Madame Schuit, a widow, who was described as an innkeeper, Mr. J. Schuit, the lighthouse-keeper and his two children, Mr. de Jong, a ship's chandler and a former pilot, and his wife, Registrar Regensburg, Madame Schwalm, who died on September 2nd in a hospital from wounds received during the catastrophe, and her two children.

A native, one of the few whose experiences were deemed worthy of remark by the Dutch language newspapers, had an extraordinary escape. The Algemeen *Dagblad* learned the story from another survivor:

We saw how three men in a canoe were thrown about by the tide, until at last the canoe overturned; the three men held on to the overturned canoe but a second big wave parted them.

Two managed to get hold of the canoe again, while the third luckily got hold of a trunk of a banana tree. An alligator approached, but he managed to keep the animal away by repeatedly putting the trunk in full length between himself and the monster.

Again a big wave struck and he had to let go of the trunk; and then, forced by necessity, as he was nearly drowning, he climbed on top of the alligator, while pressing firmly his fingers deep into the eye sockets of the monster.

The alligator floated away with him, and then by sheer accident, after some moments, met again the canoe with his two friends, who had managed to raise the craft and who now helped the modern Arion to leave his sea monster which, having been released, submerged as fast as ever before.

The wave penetrated six miles inland behind Anjer, forming a lagoon and leaving behind it large masses of coral, some pieces weighing several tons The river was choked, the cape of Anjer split in two. The lighthouse was swept away and the entire town lay in ruins. A few natives and Europeans who escaped to the hill on which stood the Residency sheltered there until the second great wave came at 7.30 a.m. It completed the destruction of Anjer, and swept them away. Shortly afterwards it grew darker than before and showers of boiling mud and pumice fell on the district, becoming wet and sticky on contact with the water. The lighthouse at Fourth Point vibrated and oscillated all night as the waves pounded the shore, the lightkeeper related afterwards.

When at 8 a.m. the *Charles Bal* passed Anjer, Captain Watson hoisted the vessel's signal letters but received no answer. He was close enough to the shore to make out the debris of houses, but he could see no movement anywhere.

Little or nothing is known of the events of the early morning along the low-lying coast to the west. Few people survived the waves in these places. Lightkeeper van Menes at Java's Second Point carefully noted each stage of the eruption:

At 1.30, 3 and 4 a.m. Strong earthquakes.
    4.30. Rain, wet ash with rain, wind S.W.
    5.30. West wind—fresh.

6.00. Still not daylight. Light still on.
7.00. Wind from N. Squall.
7.30. Sky slightly clearer.
7.45. Extinguished light—changed wicks—rain of
wet ash. Wind N.
8.00. Relit lamp—violent storm—sky completely overcast.
9.00. Weather worse. Complete darkness.

The early morning waves struck Merak at 6.15 and 7.29. After the low-lying Chinese camp was washed away on the Sunday night, the whole community took refuge on the top of the hill on which the European houses were situated. These morning waves did not reach the hilltop, and the refugees were lulled consequently into a false sense of security.

There are no reports from Tjaringin of the effect of these waves, for, after 10.30 a.m. there was no one left alive to describe them. Nor is the anonymous Englishman living at Chickandie Udik able to help us. He did not remark these waves, saying no more than that he saw a "grey band" along the horizon. The sun was not to be seen when day broke. At 7.30 a.m. it became darker and at eight o'clock he found it impossible to read without a lamp. The fact that he even tried to read, speaks highly of his British phlegm.

Across the Straits the Beyerinck family, exhausted by their five-hour journey to the slopes of Mount Radjah Bassa, lay in their hut listening to the roar of the explosions and to the wails and cries of the three thousand natives who clustered around them. Everything was smothered in ash and sheets of pumice; ash and dust fell continuously. Mrs. Beyerinck continues the story she could never forget:

At about 5.00 a.m. my husband said to one of the servants, who had faithfully stood by us, "Kill a chicken and cook some soup quickly, maybe we shall have to flee still further." I wanted to go out and see what it was like. My husband said, "I shouldn't. It will only worry you." Naturally I went in spite of what he said. But what I saw then! Thousands of tongues of fire lit up the surroundings, some only small tongues, some longer. As they disappeared they left a greenish light. Others quickly filled their

place. On tops of the trees I saw flames. I heard a crack and
noticed a sheet of fire right by me. The sea was not to be seen.
Everything was smothered in ash. I could not see my hand
before me. I went into the house again. The soup was served.
We started to eat and as far as I remember there were sixteen
of us in the room.

Mrs. Beyerinck has more to tell us of what befell on that
dreadful day. We will rejoin her later.

It was calculated after the disaster that Telok Betong, at
the head of Lampong Bay, was struck by a succession of waves
which reached the port at 2.45, 3.26, 5.44, 6.31, and 7.45 a.m.,
but according to survivors far greater damage was done by a
terrific wave that came in at 1.30 a.m. A young Dutch soldier
saw it. He was standing on a low hill at the village of Kankong,
about one thousand yards from the barracks, where he had
gone to view the destruction caused by the big wave the night
before. He saw a wave rushing into the port. He and the
villagers hastened to escape to higher ground. When he looked
back the whole village, and several others near the beach, had
disappeared. Most of the Europeans spent the night at the
Residency which was situated on a hill, 122 feet high. Our
anonymous Telok Betong correspondent, who was not able to
tell his story for two weeks, watched the waves ravage the
town. By 5 a.m. most of the houses had been washed away and
the big suspension bridge at Kotta Karang was in the process
of being destroyed by the crashing boats that had been torn
from their anchors. An hour later he watched dawn break,
finding it "really impossible to describe how beautiful was this
phenomena." Sunrise announced itself by a terrible fire glow,
such as he had never seen on normal mornings. The light, he
says, nonetheless banished all fears for the future because the
fugitives could see at last what was happening. At 9 a.m. he
went down to the beach, as he had done the night before, to
give aid to the natives who had lost their houses. The ash rain
recommenced as he reached the shore.

The *Berouw*, the *Marie*, and the *Loudon* were sheltering in
the roadstead.

Mate Stokhluysen, in command of the *Marie*, had, we recall, ordered the vessel to be battened down. Continuing his long delayed letter to his family in Holland, he told them:

> Hardly were the hatches spiked down and the port-holes closed when the first wave reached. It was a terrible moment. I thought we would perish. The boat, thanks to God, resisted the pounding waves but it was thrown on the beach. When the flood receded I was able to walk round her on dry land. After this I held counsel with the crew. They decided they did not wish to remain on board any longer for, if the wave came again, there was a risk of the boat being turned upside down and broken to pieces. I gave them permission to land. I made up my mind not to abandon the boat entrusted to me. I remained on board. The crew went off, but only some of them reached dry land. Others came back, so I had on board three women and eight men.

The big wave which came at 7.45 a.m. lifted the gunboat *Berouw*, which lay close to the pier, carried her over the crest of the shore and flung her into the Chinese quarter of the town, the first stage of her eventful "voyage," the most remarkable part of which still lay ahead.

The *Loudon* was anchored at some distance from the beach. At 1 a.m., when the weather was a little calmer, Captain Lindemann despatched a boat and six men to investigate. They rowed near the *Berouw*. It lay at anchor near the pier which was partly under water. Her captain warned the boatmen it was unsafe to land, owing to the high surf, and he told them that one boat which had tried to take off had been wrecked and its crew drowned. When the steersman reported this to Captain Lindemann he decided to await daylight. Shortly after the boat returned he heard a ship's bell which seemed to be coming nearer, and for safety he took his vessel several ship's lengths out to sea, anchoring in 9 fathoms with a 30-fathom shackle outside the hawse pipe. He heard no more of the bell. According to Lindemann the *Berouw* stranded before 7.30 a.m., for his log states:

About 7 a.m. we saw some very high seas, presumably an upheaval of the sea, approaching us up the roadstead. These seas poured themselves out upon the shore and flowed inland, so that we presumed that the inhabitants who dwelt near the shore must be drowned. The lighthouse was altogether carried away, and the *Berouw* then lay high upon the shore among the cocoanut trees. Also the revenue cutter lay aground, and some native boats which had been lying in the neighbourhood at anchor were no more to be seen.

Since it was very dangerous to stay where we were, and since if we stayed we could render no assistance, we concluded to proceed to Anjer under steam, and there to give information of what had taken place, weighed anchor at 7.30 a.m., and following the direction of the bay steered thereupon southwards.

The *Loudon,* as we shall learn later, did not go very far.

Controller Le Soeur at Pajoeng in Semanka Bay spent the night in the village quietening the frightened natives. At 4 a.m. he noticed a reddish light in the sky:

At 6 o'clock I went to the beach. The sea was so low that many cliffs were visible. It looked queer and I did not feel at ease. I called for van Zuylen, my assistant, so that we could draw up a report to the Resident about what had happened.

It was just past 7 and the lights were on. A moment later van Zuylen said "I am sorry, but I would like to stop for a moment. I don't feel at ease."

Scarcely were these words uttered when we heard a terrible noise. Then, women and children fled from their houses shouting "The water is coming. The water is coming."

Van Zuylen, the servant and I left the house in a hurry and invited everyone to take shelter in my house, which they accepted. I did so because my house was built on piles and situated on a hill.

The water once again returned to the sea. Everybody calmed down. But only for a short while because, almost at once, we heard the water approaching again with a terrible noise. 200-300 people were sheltering in my house.

I walked from one side to another to maintain peace and quiet. Suddenly I heard the front portion of the house collapse, and the water rushed in. I advised everyone to go to the rear.

But, my God, scarcely was I standing then the house collapsed completely and all of us were dragged along by the current.

I got hold of a shelf, with which I floated along until I was pulled by the legs and let go of the shelf.

After that I got hold of a few pieces of thin wood and managed to stay afloat until the water returned to the sea and I felt solid ground under my feet.

However, I stayed where I was and covered my head with my coat to protect myself against the mud rain.

I heard men, women and children call for help, but any help was impossible.

I could not raise myself out of weakness and fear and could not see a thing.

Suddenly the water returned with the same force. I said a quick prayer, asking for help for myself and everybody and prepared myself for death. The water took hold of me, turned me around and threw me away with a terrible force.

Then I got stuck between two floating houses. I couldn't breathe any more and I thought that the end was come.

But suddenly they parted and I got hold of a banana trunk and stuck to it with all my strength. I don't know how long I floated around, but again the water returned to the sea and once again I stood on solid ground.

Again I sat there for at least an hour without moving and it was dark everywhere and the mud rain was still going on. I did hear people shout, but that was all.

A moment later I heard a native talking to a few women. I called out to them and proposed we walk along together, which was accepted. I left my place with closed eyes and touched the ground all around, leaving the sea behind me. I did not have any clothes on any more, except a vest which was badly torn anyway, so I walked stark naked in the cold and mud rain.

Soon I discovered that the three persons had departed, as I did not hear them any more.

I would have given a thousand guilders if I could only have refound my previous place, as where I was walking now the ground was covered with thorns and nasty bushes, and all the time I fell over trees and the debris of houses.

Walking along for sometime, I at last heard voices again. I

opened my eyes and saw a native with some women. I told them I was the Controller, and together we reached Penanggoenga that evening at 8 o'clock. My ordeal had lasted from 8 in the morning until 8 in the evening.

Another survivor from Semanka Bay described afterwards how a second wave followed the first, roaring up the beach, destroying the houses left by the first wave. It then became quite dark, with mud and ashes pouring down.

The crews of the vessels sheltering at the eastern entrance to the Strait passed the night without undue alarm, Captain Baker of the *W. H. Besse* writing in his log:

> The sun when it arose next morning had the appearance of a ball of fire, the air so smoky, could see but a short distance. At 6 a.m. thinking the worst of the eruption was over, as the reports were not so frequent nor so heavy as during the night, got under weigh and, having a fair wind, was in hopes to get out clear of the Straits before nightfall.

As the logs of the other ships waiting at the entrance to the Straits make no reference to unusual events during the early hours of Monday, we can conclude that there was nothing particular to remark. At 4.30 a.m., Captain Strachan of the *Anerley* recorded: "Before daylight the whole heavens were lighted up by a pale yellow light of changing hues, which lit up the entire ship and turned everything on board the same colour. This lasted 45 minutes and then died out. Daylight, such as it was, broke about 6 a.m."

The *Koningin Emma der Nederlander* was in dock at Onrust Island in Batavia Bay. On board, Lieutenant G. F. Tydemann noted at 5.30 a.m. a thin fine ash falling in grains, some sharp, others smooth, round and soft, all easily ground to powder between finger and thumb, and crunching under shoes as it lay on deck. The ash rain interrupted the daily routine, he says, and everyone on board was affected by a feeling of fear and dread of what the ash might portend. The fall of ash caused the day's programme to be rearranged, the mate finding work for all in clearing it from the vessel's decks, a desire for cleanliness which had to be abandoned as the ash rain became denser and the sky redder and redder. The mate's face, says Tydemann, became darker as he angrily surveyed the soft ash spreading over everything, spoiling the elbow grease of a week's work.

When morning broke in Batavia the light was found to be obscured. The sun did not shine, and the whole sky seemed overcast in a very strange manner. At about seven o'clock a shower of ashes commenced to fall, and a general feeling of alarm began to be felt as to the appalling nature of the outburst, and the fate of those places nearer to it than Batavia. The fall was intermittent until the business day began in the Old Town. Then the sky became pale yellow and more obscure. The ash shower was very dense, giving a deadness to the sounds of life, and leading to a kind of suffocating feeling. The gloom rapidly deepened and it became quite dark, so that lamps had to be lit in offices and houses. Fifteen hundred burners were alight at 9 a.m., calculated the engineer in charge at the gasworks. The pressure gauge, he noted, had made several remarkable jumps at 1.55, 5.43 and 6.57 in the morning, as the result of some outside agency. Shortly after 9.15 a.m. shattering explosions shook the city, breaking windows, crushing walls and shaking houses. One frightful concussion extinguished all the lights, leaving Batavia in complete darkness. A silent feeling of dread took possession of everyone. Little business was done and most persons in the city went home to their families to be ready for any catastrophe that might terminate these fearful appearances.

A hundred miles inland, at Buitenzorg, Verbeek heard a terrible explosion at 6.45 a.m. The people of the town who had been trying to catch up with lost sleep leapt out of bed, lamps fell out of their sockets, whitewash flaked off walls and doors, and windows banged. "It was a real din," Verbeek remarks. After 7 a.m. darkness came on rapidly, extending as far as Tjandja, 130 miles from Krakatoa, and Bandong, 150 miles distant.

7. Crack of Doom

IT WAS now 10 a.m. on that memorable Monday. A pall of ash blanketed the Straits of Sunda. The darkness extended for a hundred miles. According to one estimate the dust cloud rose to an altitude of fifty miles, making a box of inky blackness. Krakatoa's roar died to a murmur. To thousands of exhausted people the sudden silence brought the hope that the volcano was in retreat, its fires extinguished, its eruption exhausted. The appearance of tranquillity was deceptive; the Crack of Doom was but a step away.

At ten o'clock plus two minutes, three-quarters of Krakatoa Island, eleven square miles of its surface, an area not much less than Manhattan, a mass of rock and earth one and one-eighth cubic miles in extent, collapsed into the chasm beneath. Nineteen hours of continuous eruption had drained the magma from the chamber faster than it could be replenished from below. Their support removed, thousands of tons of roof rock crashed into the void below. Krakatoa's three cones caved in. The sea bed reared and opened in upheaval. The sea rushed into the gaping hole. From the raging cauldron of seething rocks, frothing magma and hissing sea, spewed an immense quantity of water. Up from the volcano shot huge rocks. A cloud of dust and debris rose high in the air.

From the volcano roared a mighty blast, Krakatoa's death cry, the greatest volume of sound recorded in human history. It was heard 3,000 miles away, over a great circle 4,500 miles wide. Yet, by a queer freak of nature, nearby hardly anyone noticed it or remarked its intensity. The world's loudest noise

94

was screened by layers of ash permeating the atmosphere, and it fell upon ears already stunned and deafened.

A tempest of wind blew upwards and outwards from Krakatoa. Before it died away it circled the earth seven and one-half times.

From the truncated island swirled a wall of water, rolling outward in an ever widening circle. This huge mass of sea water crossed the Straits in all directions, mounting in height as the sea bed shallowed. Rearing to mountainous size as it approached the shore, it rampaged up breaches, rolled across the countryside and clawed at hills, destroying everything and everyone in its path. It funnelled into a wedge-shaped bore, at least a hundred feet high, at the Strait's narrow eastern entrance. It escaped freely through its wide western end, sweeping across the Indian Ocean, touching at Cape Horn, and rolling up the Atlantic. Two days after it left Krakatoa, it lapped the shores of the English Channel, 11,500 miles away, raising water levels by two inches.

Around the shores of the Sunda Strait, the wave killed thousands of people, drowning, lashing and battering. How many people died between thirty and sixty minutes from the time the wave left Krakatoa can never be determined exactly, for no one can estimate how many of the 36,417 known casualties of the disaster were already dead. Many of these people probably perished suddenly and quickly under the weight and power of the great killer wave. The official figure may be too low for it was an approximation based on the number of towns and villages destroyed, many of which disappeared without leaving any trace.

Several of the survivors attempted to describe the great wave. The magnitude of the experience was too great for them. The sight of the grey wall of water appearing from nowhere was an experience which no one could have described adequately. The air was filled with swirling dust and falling pumice. It was blacker than the blackest night. Huge tracts of land were submerged. Towns and houses were in ruins. Corpses lay everywhere. The wave came without warning.

It rose higher than the highest palm tree. It was preceded and
followed by a tempest of wind. It dwarfed everything. It was
a towering wall of solid water. It moved at tremendous speed.
People were submerged before they knew what struck them.
In an instant they were floundering and struggling in foaming
water, jerking, pulling, dragging and shoving them. They were
hurled into a maelstrom of tossing, twisting, black chaos. Those
who stood on high ground did not wait to watch Nature's
wonder; they turned to run in precipitous, gasping, tortured
flight.

The spectacle of Krakatoa's grand collapse, flashing explosion
and great wave, a stupendous manifestation of Nature's might,
was enacted unseen. No one saw it all. A tiny number of survivors witnessed bits of it in the limited compass of their own
experience. They did their best to tell us what happened.

By 9.15 a.m. the *Charles Bal* had reached a spot somewhere
between Java's Third and Fourth points, and the barque was
then about thirty miles from Krakatoa. The sea was like glass,
the weather looking much finer, says Captain Watson. The fall
of ash had ceased. Shortly after 10 a.m. he heard a tremendous
explosion:

We saw a wave rush on to Button Island, apparently sweeping right over the south part, and rising halfway up the north
and east sides. This we saw repeated twice, but the helmsman
says he saw it once before we looked. The same wave seemed
also to run right on to the Java shore. At the same time the sky
rapidly covered in, the wind came strong from south-west by
south. By 10.30 we were enclosed in a darkness that might almost be felt, and at the same time there commenced a downpour of mud, sand, and I know not what; ship going north-east
by north, seven knots per hour under three lower topsails; put
out the side lights, placed two men on the look-out forward, and
one man employed washing the mud off the binnacle glass. We
had seen two vessels to the north and north-west of us before
the sky closed in, adding much to the anxiety of our position.
The darkness was so intense we had to grope our way about the
decks, and although speaking to each other on the poop, yet

could not see each other. This horrible spate and downpour of mud continued until 12.30 p.m., the roarings of the volcano and the lightnings being something fearful.

Captain Watson's reference to *two* vessels in the vicinity of his ship is mystifying. One of them could have been the *Loudon,* which, as we shall see, had commenced her voyage back to Anjer. The presence of another ship close to Krakatoa is accounted for by a quotation from the Australian newspaper, the Sydney *Mail,* in which the captain of the *Amora* recalled his experiences while passing through the Straits of Sunda on August 27th. He states no time, but we may deduce from his narrative that the story refers to the explosion at 10.02 a.m.:

> One magnificent blaze of light proceeded from Krakatoa's top. Higher and higher the blaze seemed to mount as we drew closer to its base, while the sound had become one continuous roar, like hundreds of blasts from some mighty furnace; a volume of smoke extended from it for miles, like a funeral pyre. As we passed through, some of the fine dust and strong sulphurous fumes of the subterranean upheavals got into my eyes, and filled our throats, causing us to keep under the awnings till we passed, glad to leave the island on our lea. We could then admire its splendid upheaval and listen to its mighty roar without fear. There seemed to be a strange vibration in the water and ship while we were passing. The flames looked grand as, leaping high in the heavens with a mighty roar, they sent their sulphurous fumes miles upwards, and then, dying out till they seemed expended, would leap upwards with renewed force and fury. This continued till the ship carried us farther and farther away and the sound got weaker. We passed 3–4 miles from the volcano.

The *Berbice* must have been no more than fifty miles westward of Krakatoa, yet Captain Logan did not remark the great explosion at 10.02 a.m. He certainly experienced the great wave as his log shows:

> A high continuous wind set in from the south-east, which veering afterwards made the ship list considerably from the weight of ash on our masts and rigging. A heavy sea came rush-

ing on. It rose to a height of 20 feet, swept over the ship, making her quiver from stem to stern with the shock. Meanwhile the storm continued. The mercurial barometer did not stand still for a single moment, but incessantly went up and down from 28 to 30 inches. When I went to examine my chronometers I found that they had all stopped, probably owing to the shaking of the ship from the concussions. The darkness and the storm continued, but the sea became calmer. The flashes of light showed it to be covered with pumice and ash on all sides.

The killer wave struck the Javanese coast, reaching Tjaringin, thirty miles across the Straits, at 10.32 a.m., it was calculated afterwards. There were then probably few people alive to see it. The low-lying town, or what was left of it after the early waves had struck, was swept away entirely, a giant durian tree, maimed of its branches, remaining as the only landmark of the once prosperous town. A wall of water rushed over the shore, destroying the harbour works, the European and the Chinese quarters, and depositing huge lumps of coral from five to seven miles inland. Ten thousand people, it was estimated, died that morning at Tjaringin. Controller van Tromp was one of the few Dutchmen saved. Military Supervisor Hoffman turned back to rescue his maps and he was drowned. All fifty-five members of the Regent's family perished. The deputy collector of taxes, who refused to flee, was found forty-eight hours later still seated on his precious cash box.

The Europeans who died at Tjaringin included Assistant Resident J. A. O. van den Bosch, Topographical Service Lieutenant, A. F. Dessauvagies, Supervisor P. Schalk, Mme. Berlauwt (who was also known as the widow Stralendorff), the patih (an official less than a Regent but higher than a headman), whose body was found headless, and the headman and all his family.

The wide plain extending round Pepper Bay was submerged for many miles. Nowhere did the sea reach further inland. It submerged the town of Penimbang, ten miles from the coast, and, in one place, it was still thirty feet high, three miles from the coast. The sea burst into the village of Tjelegon with enormous speed, sweeping everything away. Not a stone of the old port was left standing. The wave came so fast that refugees who turned back to save their possessions were caught and drowned. Banyan trees two hundred years old were uprooted and swept along in the flood, killing and maiming the fugitives. Tanara, another village on the coast, shared the same fate, and seven hundred corpses were found there. At Tjeringur, the harbour works were swept away and the sea rushed several miles inland. Two other towns disappeared entirely. The market at Karang Antoe was thronged just as the wave broke over the shore; when rescuers reached the town they found the bazaar filled with corpses, mostly those of the women who kept the stalls. In all, three hundred people are believed to have perished there.

Most of the lighthouses along the Java shore were destroyed, and the whole coastline was changed. At a village on Welcome Bay, Supervisor van Heutz saved himself by climbing a tree, from where he was rescued two days later. The widow Buijs saw both her husband and her son drowned before her eyes. She was quite unable to tell rescuers how she herself was saved. "It was God's will" was all she could say. At Second Point, Lightkeeper van Menes noted the time of each occurrence, though whether his observations were correct seems doubtful. He recorded a great explosion at "11.00 a.m. or after," noting that doors and windows banged violently. Ten minutes later lightning struck the conductor and broke it, and killed four of the ten convicts working there, those who were chained in iron collars. Menes succeeded in clambering into the lighthouse, which withstood the shock of the great wave. From his window he watched the waves tearing at the stonework, and he remarked that "the sea itself seemed to be on fire," meaning, it has been suggested, that it was filled with the burning debris of trees and houses, set alight by overturned household lamps and fires.

Anjer had been destroyed completely in the early hours of the morning. Not one survivor remained to tell the tale of how the great wave overwhelmed what was left of the town.

The telegraph operator, Schruit's assistant, who returned to the coast about 10 a.m., saw "the ocean advancing like an enormous rampart of water." He fled to higher ground, hearing an "awful roaring noise as the sea struck the land."

Telegraph Master Schruit, who had escaped to Kares two and one-half miles away, had by 9.30 a.m. walked with other refugees about a mile on his return to Anjer, when, all of a sudden, "we heard a frightful sound in the direction of Krakatoa, followed by a heavy fall of ashes and flashes of lightning. We continued our march, and heard in quick succession four more claps of thunder, after which the noise calmed by degrees. Then commenced a heavy mud rain which was terrific in the extreme. Many escaped natives from Anjer came to meet us, making loud lamentations and calling out *'Ayer datang, tuan, tuan ada di blakan.'* ('Water coming, the gentlemen are behind.') Immediately on this warning we took a cross cut and ran till we reached the village of Jabat. The occupants of this village, which consisted of four or five houses, dragged us in as it were; and as it had become pitch dark notwithstanding the mud rain, they came out to meet us with torches. It was evident that these poor people were glad to see Europeans amongst them, and that their presence diminished their dread and anxiety."

Evidently, though he heard the big bang, Schruit did not see the great wave:

> At that moment the weather was most dreadful, the cracking of the trees, the snapping off of bamboos, the heavy rain and the thick darkness combined to make me think it an image of hell. In the place where I found myself there were about a hundred and fifty people who had fled from the surrounding dangers, Chinese and natives together; and as I observed some of them drinking water in a reckless manner, I made enquiries as to the supply, and at once took possession of all there was at hand. The number of refugees continued to increase, and as their first cry was for water, I began to fear that necessity of life would run short. So I sat upon the water vat, and quenched the thirst of the crowd by means of small draughts.

But the little crowd was by no means so quiet and still as natives and Chinese usually are in the presence of Europeans. They began to lament their hard lot and to complain more or less against the Government who, by the war against Atjeh, was the cause of all the disasters. Towards me and the other Europeans they were however very obliging, and they seemed to derive consolation from our assurances. They followed our movements, and declared that they would go wherever we went.

At first, going any further was out of the question, for each and all had need of rest. There was no help for it. Schruit and his companions stayed where they were.

The lighthouse at Fourth Point, which had withstood the lashing and battering of the early waves, succumbed to the fury of the great wave. Yet by a miracle, the lightkeeper was saved. He saw his wife and child drowned before his eyes. The stone-built lighthouse, reinforced with iron, withstood the violent sea, until an enormous stone, carried by the wave, smashed its base, bringing it down in ruins. "The lightkeeper related the story, in the resigned way of a Javanese," remarks Captain van Doorn, to whom he repeated it some weeks later. "Then, as if it was the most natural thing to do, he resumed his duties, lighting the temporary light."

By 10.40 a.m. Anjer was a waste of water. Nothing remained, not even the stone tomb of General Cathcart (a British officer who lost his life near the town in 1812 during the British occupation). Not one of its massive stone slabs was left standing.

The unknown Englishman living at Chikandie Udik near Anjer does not mention, in his story, either the great explosion or the big wave, saying only, "It grew darker and darker until a darkness like that of night set in. At ten o'clock the hand held before the eyes could not be discerned. A high wind blew and showers of ashes and sand fell. The following hours were terrible," he related; several words which express his feelings poignantly.

There are very few native survivor-stories of the Javanese disaster. "At the time of the eruption of Krakatoa I was about ten years old," eighty-three-year-old Yasim told an interviewer in 1956. He lived in the little village of Waluran, about a mile from Anjer, and from Yasim's description, the interviewer drew a plan of the village. By the shore were situated the boat sheds of Yasim's father, who was a fisherman, and behind them stood a group of houses, including the headman's, and the mosque. The village was flanked by plantations. "The waves came three times," recalled Yasim. The houses, the boat sheds, the fort with all its guns were swept away. The mosque, filled with frightened people, was dragged into the sea. Yasim ran and ran, reaching high ground before the last great wave came roaring up. He saw it pass over the tops of palm trees that were fifty feet high. At another village, a boy named Djikoneng was caught by the wave and thrown into a tree. When he regained consciousness, he saw that the land was empty. Everything, men, animals, houses, the lighthouse were gone. Where they had stood was a mass of raging waters. Only fifteen inhabitants of the village survived, he told his interviewer seventy-three years later, lifting the scarf from his head to show a huge scar. "The wave did that," he recalled.

One European and one native only survived at Merak. Twenty-seven hundred of its inhabitants died, including thirteen Europeans, among whom were K. A. Naumann and his wife, Overseer H. B. van Diest and his wife, Overseer J. Kaal, Machinist S. C. van Essen, his wife and four children, Storekeeper T. S. Townsend and his child.

The story of their deaths is one of the strangest of the whole disaster, for they were sheltered on top of the hill behind the town. It was 130 feet high, yet the great wave roared up its slopes and destroyed all the stone-built European houses on its top, leaving only the foundation of Naumann's house. Works Accountant E. Peckler saw the wave coming. He ran further up the hill, the wave gaining upon him. He fell exhausted, expecting to be engulfed. Looking back he saw the wave rushing towards him. Heaving himself up, he ran further, falling on his knees and losing consciousness. When he regained his senses, he saw the wave receding. All the houses were gone. Engineer Abell also saw the wave. He left Merak at 7.30 that morning to report to his chief in Batavia. Looking back from the mountain road, he saw "a colossal wave" roaring up the shore. It was higher than the highest coconut palm, he recalled later. No one in its path could have survived, he told his chief. The wall of water rushed over the land, looking like something he could not have "dreamed in a nightmare."

Much argument developed after the disaster, about the height of the wave at Merak and at other places. The eye-witnesses had exaggerated, it was claimed by sober-minded critics. Nonetheless, Peckler's story is corroborated by the height on the hill over which the wave broke. The wave must have been 130 feet high at Merak, as he claimed. Elsewhere the greatest height claimed for the wave was 67–100 feet at Tjaringin and 50 feet at Princess Island. The colossal height the wave reached at Merak was due, no doubt, to the situation of that port at the narrow entrance to the Straits, where the water was compressed between the two shores.

The great wave, rearing in height as it roared through the narrow eastern entrance of the Strait, partially destroyed the island of Thwart-the-way, where an unknown number of people perished, and submerged completely the islands of Sebessi and Sebukoe. The inhabitants of Sebessi, three thousand of them, were drowned. The other island was fortunately uninhabited.

Seaman Dalby was working on the *Hope,* anchored off St. Nicholas Point, helping to get the cargo unloaded into the lighters lying alongside. Krakatoa's eruption appeared to be finished. The morning was blazing and brilliant. The sun, rising like a ball of shining brass, promised a scorching and pitilessly hot day. A pall of blackness lay to the west, blotting out the Straits. Dalby told what then happened in his radio broadcast in 1937.

About ten o'clock there seemed something strange about the weather and, as always on sailing ships, weird groans and whistles, scarcely audible, came from the rigging. Gradually the

brilliant morning changed to an ominous dullness and the wind
came in strong gusts. Sharp orders came from the poop. The
lighters, alongside, made off as quickly as possible, some of our
coolies tumbling into them. I fancy it was their last tumble. All
hands became busy making everything fast and getting another
anchor out ready to let go in case of emergency. It got darker
and darker. The rumblings got louder; they seemed all round
us. The gusts of wind increased to a hurricane such as no man
aboard had ever experienced. The wind seemed a solid mass
pushing everything before it, and roaring like a huge steam-
engine, shrieking through the rigging like demons in torment.

It became absolutely pitch dark, with flashes of vivid lightning
which almost blinded us. The thunder was deafening. We followed the officers around to make sure of anything that looked
like breaking away. We let go the other anchor, and officers
and seamen were watching the cables all the day. We were
fearful of our anchors, but they held. When we got a glimpse
of the heavens we could see a terrible commotion going on. The
clouds were whirling round at terrific speed. Most of us thought
we were in the vortex of a cyclone, but, as the noise became
louder and louder, I at any rate reckoned it was something
volcanic, especially when about noon it rained a continuous
downpour of dust. This seemed a sulphurous gritty sort of stuff,
and as we had only about two cotton garments on, everyone
was smothered all over, burned, choked and almost blinded.

Visibility at this time was about a yard. I seemed isolated,
and felt my way about the deck, never loosing my hold of anything handy. No one could imagine the force of the wind. Occa-
sionally I met others on the same lay as myself, but quite
unrecognisable, just moving grey objects. Ropes and lines were
lashing across the decks like whips. Once I noticed two terrified
eyes belonging to a poor old coolie peeping from under a boat.

The noise was terrible, especially one great bang about noon,
which is supposed to have been the loudest noise ever heard
on earth. It shook the people out of their beds at Batavia,
ninety miles away. It was the top of Krakatoa blowing up into
the skies. Not that we knew or cared what it was. The whole
heavens seemed a blaze of fire and the clouds formed such
fantastic shapes as to look startlingly unnatural; at times they
hung down like ringlets of hair, some jet black, others dirty
white.

Seventy-seven-year-old Dalby was a little hazy about his facts. The great bang he noted at noon happened, we know, two hours earlier and there could then have been few people in bed at Batavia. His statement that Krakatoa blew her top into the skies reflects an often repeated and incorrect version of what took place at the volcano.

Following the great explosion at 10.02, ships sheltering outside the Straits were flung high on the crest of the mountainous wave that bored through the narrow gap between Java and Sumatra. "I am writing this blind in pitch darkness," Captain Sampson of the *Norham Castle* noted in his log; "we are under a continual rain of pumice-stone and dust. So violent are the explosions that the ear-drums of over half my crew have been shattered. My last thoughts are with my dear wife. I am convinced that the Day of Judgment has come." A mile away, Captain Strachan on the *Anerley* recorded his observations: "At 10.00 a.m. it was so dark that the crew had to light all the lights. Barometer rising and falling ½ inch to 1 inch in the minute. Ashes and pumice-stones falling."

The most detailed story comes from the log of the American three-master, *W. H. Besse,* which, since dawn, had been moving into the Straits. At 10 a.m. Captain Baker's vessel was southeast of Sebessi Island and within six miles of St. Nicholas Point when "we heard some terrible reports, also observed a heavy black bank rising up from the direction of Krakatoa Island, the barometer fell an inch at one jump, suddenly rising and falling an inch at a time; called all hands, furled all sails securely, which was scarcely done before the squall struck the ship with terrific force; let go port anchor and all the chains in the locker; wind increasing to a hurricane; let go starboard anchor; it had been gradually growing dark since 9 a.m., and by the time the squall struck us it was darker than any night I ever saw. It was midnight at noon. A heavy shower of ashes came with the squall, the air being so thick it was difficult to breathe, also noticed strong smell of sulphur, all hands expecting to be suffocated; terrible noises from the volcano, the sky filled with forked lightning, running in all directions, and making the darkness more intense than ever.

The howling of the wind through the rigging formed one of the wildest and most awful scenes imaginable, one that never will be forgotten by anyone on board, all expecting that the last days of the earth had come. The water was running by us in the direction of the volcano at the rate of 12 miles per hour."

Captain Baker's observation of the current running in the *direction* of Krakatoa, an apparently strange phenomena, not otherwise remarked, provided an important clue which, as we shall learn later, assisted in explaining the exact course of events at the volcano.

Natives sent on reconnaissance by Controller Beyerinck at 6 a.m. returned to the hut on the slopes of Mount Radjah Bassa to report that Kalimbang had disappeared. The great wave which came at 10.30 a.m. swept in unobserved, but Mrs. Beyerinck seems to be describing the aftereffects of the Big Bang:

> Someone burst in shouting "shut the doors, shut the doors." Suddenly it was pitch dark. The last thing I saw was the ash being pushed up through the cracks in the floor-boards, like a fountain.
>
> I turned to my husband and heard him say in despair "Where is the knife? The knife on the table. I will cut all our wrists, then we shall be sooner released from our suffering." The knife could not be found.
>
> I felt a heavy pressure, throwing me to the ground. Then it seemed as if all the air was being sucked away and I could not breathe. Large lumps clattered down on my head, my back and my arms. Each lump was larger than the others. I could not stand.
>
> I don't think I lost consciousness for I heard the natives praying and crying *"Allah il Allah."*
>
> I felt people rolling over me. I was kicked and I felt a foot on part of my body.
>
> No sound came from my husband or children. Only part of my brain could have been working for I didn't realise I had been burnt and everything which came in contact with me was

hot ash, mixed with moisture. I remember thinking, I want to get up and go outside. But I could not. My back was powerless.

After much effort I did finally manage to get to my feet but I could not straighten my back or neck. I felt as if a heavy iron chain was fastened around my neck and was pulling me downwards.

Propping my hands on my knees, I tottered, doubled-up, to the door. I knew it was in the corner. It was stuck fast. I fell to my knees in the ash.

Later I noticed that the door was ajar and I forced myself through the opening. I looked for the stairs. I tripped and fell. I realised the ash was hot and I tried to protect my face with my hands. The hot bite of the pumice pricked like needles.

My long hair, which reached to my knees, usually knotted in a tight bun, was loose.

Without thinking I walked hopefully forward. Had I been in my right mind I would have understood what a dangerous thing it was to do, to leave the vicinity of that house and plunge into the hellish darkness.

Then came sudden, terrifying stillness.

When I had walked about 15 paces, still in my doubled-up position, I stubbed my toe on something very peculiar. I ran up against large and small branches and did not even think of avoiding them. I entangled myself more and more in that nightmare of branches, all entirely stripped of leaves.

My hair got caught up, and each time with a twist of the head I managed to free myself. Then something got hooked into my finger and hurt. I noticed for the first time that the skin was hanging off everywhere, thick and moist from the ash stuck to it. Thinking it must be dirty, I wanted to pull bits of skin off, but that was still more painful. My tired brain could not make out what it was. I did not know I had been burned.

Worn out, I leaned against a tree.

We shall hear of Mrs. Beyerinck again.

The narrow shores of Lampong Bay squeezed the water into a compact mass. It reared to mammoth size as it rushed towards Telok Betong.

8. Killer Wave

THE EUROPEANS assembled on Residency Hill at Telok Betong welcomed the dawn with sighs of relief. The first streaks of light dispelled the gloom of the long night. They were out of reach of the waves that had done so much damage in the town. The rain of ash and pumice was annoying and no one was particularly disturbed when it increased about 9.30 a.m. When Krakatoa's violent explosion was heard shortly after ten o'clock, "everyone was frozen with horror" tersely stated the Resident in his report. The great wave reached the town at three minutes past eleven.

One European, the man whom we can identify only by his story which appeared in the Java *Bode* on September 19th, was down at the shore helping to rescue natives from their demolished houses. He was occupied in dragging a beam from a man who had been trapped in the debris of his house, when he heard a scream. Looking seaward he saw the wave approaching at terrifying speed, accompanied by a thunderous noise. The vision of this enormous wave called, he wrote, for the putting into practice of the general principle of *sauve qui peut*. He ran. In his flight he witnessed scenes too horrible to remember; incidents that reminded him of the animal instinct that enables people to do the impossible. He could not aid the poor natives, running ahead of the wave. He saw a mother collapsing under the weight of her baby, too dear to abandon to save her own life. He saw another woman who "as a result of her fright and despair gives birth to a child while walking on."

Whipped on by fear and despair the refugees reached the

top of the hill. Hundreds of families were gathered there. Suddenly they heard a heavy explosion. "For one terrible moment we expected the worst," the European storyteller recalled. Suddenly day changed into night; a rain of ash began to fall, thicker than the severest tropical storm. There came repeated thunder flashes; they were accompanied by an amazing fire column which gave the sky a terrible appearance so that, he says, "one's heart nearly stopped beating." On all sides trees fell and branches were snapped off by the weight of ash and mud. Complete trees were uprooted. "In that situation we remained until 9 o'clock that evening when the rain of ash stopped," he briefly describes, omitting many of the facts we would like to know.

Fortunately the Javanese newspapers supplied some of them. The great wave reached within six feet of the top of a hill which was 122 feet above sea level. Calculations subsequently made computed its height at Telok Betong as eighty-seven feet. The official report states that there was "general panic" on the hilltop as the wave roared up. The town was destroyed completely. Strongly built houses were torn from their foundations; heavy treasure chests, anchored to the ground by strong bolts, were carried like straws and dashed against the hill, three hundred yards away. Five thousand people died in Telok Betong and its neighbourhood, three Europeans and 2,260 natives in the town itself.

The wave lifted the gunboat *Berouw,* a vessel having a draft of six feet, carrying four guns, and having a complement of four Europeans and twenty-four natives, from where she had been deposited in the Chinese quarter, carried her up the valley of the Koeripan River and deposited the vessel at a spot one and one-eighth miles inland, leaving her stranded thirty feet above sea level, behind a hill. All her crew were killed. The vessel's bones lie at that place still, a perpetual reminder of Krakatoa's might.

Mate Stokhluysen on the *Marie,* when he saw three waves approaching, no longer doubted his last hour had come. His vessel was thrown on the beach in such a way that the waves could smash down on it with all their force and might. Stokhluysen said a short prayer. He thought all was over and he waited with resignation for what was bound to happen as the waves pounded the *Marie*. It was totally dark. He heard an explosion which seemed like that of a powder magazine. The sky was on fire, the air asphyxiating. A rain of ash fell without interruption. There was no light. The *Marie* jerked about continually. Stokhluysen did not know where he was. After some hours of battering the *Marie* was thrown high and dry on the beach.

The experiences of the people on the *Loudon* supply us now with two descriptions of the disaster. N. van Sandick, an engineer on board, gives this account:

Suddenly we saw a gigantic wave of prodigious height advancing from the sea-shore with considerable speed. Immediately the crew set to under great pressure and managed after a fashion to set sail in face of the imminent danger; the ship had just enough time to meet with the wave from the front. After a moment, full of anguish, we were lifted up with a dizzy rapidity. The ship made a formidable leap, and immediately afterwards we felt as though we had plunged into the abyss. But the ship's blade went higher and we were safe. Like a high mountain, the monstrous wave precipitated its journey towards the land. Immediately afterwards another three waves of colossal size appeared. And before our eyes this terrifying upheaval of the sea, in a sweeping transit, consumed in one instant the ruin of the town; the lighthouse fell in one piece, and all the houses of the town were swept away in one blow like a castle of cards. All was finished. There, where a few moments ago lived the town of Telok Betong, was nothing but the open sea.

The steamer *Berouw* was lifted by the flood and from the side of the ship we could see it thrown over the jetty head at the level of the cocoa palm trees. The natives' houses, built of the style having a clear space of the height of about a yard underneath, were an easy prey for the wave, which lifted and destroyed them. But the brick houses of the Dutch people were as easily destroyed. They were torn from their foundations and lost in the sea.

We cannot find the words to describe the terrifying events which left us with the sight of such a cataclysm. The thunder-striking suddenness of the changing light, the gigantic propor-tions of the spectacle, the unexpected devastation which was accomplished in an instant before our eyes, all this left us stupefied, without at first realising what a disturbing phenome-non had taken place. There was transformation, an instant changing of the light, as at a fairy-scene, at the wave of a magic wand. Do not imagine that what passed before our eyes was a fanciful trifling, but certainly a terrible reality, which claimed millions of human lives in the speed of a wink of the eye. What frightening and incalculable ruins were strewn there in one moment. What an incredible force was possessed by that sea, the flood of which, in one blow, destroyed an entire city, which man had had so much difficulty in building and so long to erect.

We, spectators of the upheaval, were now menaced by a great peril, and before us stood a terrible and inevitable death. All that the most active imagination could evoke, all that the most fertile mind could conceive, was far, far remote from the horrible, frightful situation in which we found ourselves.

By comparison with his passenger's story, Captain Linde-mann's narrative is prosaic. Shortly after ten o'clock, it be-came so dark that the captain, who had started to move his ship out of the roadstead, intending to return to Anjer, could not see the outlines of either the vessel or the individuals of his crew. He brought his vessel to a sudden stop by dropping one anchor. Ash and pumice, some pieces several inches thick, rained on deck. By 10.30 a.m. "we were in total darkness," he noted in the log. The needle of the compass became violently agitated; the barometer went extremely high; breathing be-came difficult. Several members of the crew were affected and became ill. The wind increased. It reached the force of a hurri-cane. Captain Lindemann took measures to meet the danger:

So we let down both anchors and kept the screw turning slowly at half speed in order to ride over the terribly high seas which kept suddenly striking us presumably in consequence of a "sea quake" and made us dread being buried under them.

Awnings and curtains from forward right up to the main-mast, three boat covers, and the uppermost awning of the quarter deck were blown away in a moment. Some objects on deck which had been lashed got loose and were carried over-board; the upper deck hatchways and those on the main deck were closed tightly, and the passengers for the most part were sent below. Heavy storms. The lightning struck the mainmast conductor six or seven times, but did no damage. The rain of pumice-stones changed to a violent mud rain, and this mud rain was so heavy that in the space of ten minutes the mud lay half a foot deep.

Kept steaming with the head of the ship as far as possible seawards for half an hour when the sea began to abate, and at noon the wind dropped away entirely. Then we stopped the engine. The darkness however remained as before, as did also the mud rain. The barometer at that time stood again at 763.25 millims. Sounded the pumps. No water. Let the crew and also such passengers as were on deck work at throwing the mud overboard. At 2 p.m. the barometer was 763.30. The mud rain changed into a light ash rain.

Captain Lindemann determined to make for Anjer.

The wave reached the head of Semanka Bay shortly after it had destroyed Telok Betong. It was not quite so high as in Lampong Bay, but it was sufficiently strong to devastate the entire coastline and to destroy dozens of villages and towns.

At the village of Beneawany, 2,500 natives, who had as-sembled to meet the Resident, perished, and at Pajoeng, Con-troller Le Soeur's clerk, van Zuylen, was killed. Three hundred and twenty-seven people disappeared at Tandjoengan and at Tanot Bringin, and 244 at Beteong. Not a house was left standing at Tampang. At Benkolen lighthouse, the wave rose forty-five feet around its walls, and it demolished a building constructed of iron and stone. Ten of the convicts working at the lighthouse were drowned, and Lightkeeper Hamwyck was severely wounded. He was caught in the kitchen of his house and became stuck under debris. He freed himself after a long struggle and reached the lighthouse, losing on the way his logbook in which he had noted details of the disaster to that time. His assistant was drowned, and two out of five of his native helpers were wounded, as were four convicts.

The controller of Kroe, the zealous Dr. Horst, survived, and he arrived in Batavia two weeks later, flourishing his record of the phenomena he witnessed on that fearful day.

6.00 a.m.	Sky grey. Sun observed. Rains of ash.
8-10 a.m.	Fine ash. No sound heard.
10.10 a.m.	Temperature 73° F. Sky all obscured. Too dark to write. Sky streaked with lightning. Darkness increases.
10.30	Total night. Thunder continues.
11.00	Darker than night. Cinder falls. Doors and windows closed. All openings stuffed up to keep out fire and ash.
12.00	Thick darkness surrounds us. Ash finer. Less noise. Continual thunder. Crackling explosions. Thermometer 73° F. Ash lessens. Wind turns W.
12.30 p.m.	Thick darkness. Ash almost ceased. Lightning and thunder.

The great wave affected the shores of the west and east coasts of Sumatra and in both districts explosions were heard, coastal areas were inundated, and people drowned. Noordwatcher Island, off Sumatra's east coast, was submerged and waves broke into the lighthouse where Keeper H. van der Meulen was watching the ships lying at the mouth of the Straits. The big wave came at 11.30, he told his rescuers three days later.

Eastern Bantam suffered severely. The huge wave swept round St. Nicholas Point and down the coast towards Batavia. A number of villages were submerged and many lives were lost. Several people were killed at Pegadoengan. At the lighthouse, built upon a high rock, the sea roared past unseen in the darkness. One hundred and twenty survivors from various villages took refuge in the lighthouse, where two of them died from exhaustion. At Prince Island, a priest and fifty-five natives perished.

At Tangerang, ash fell at 10 a.m., and by 11 it was completely dark. Visibility was nil and lamps were lit. Auctioneer Gronjin and his two clerks, Frans and Jacobs, had gone to the village of Kramat to conduct a sale. Before it started, the sky became dark, and they decided to return to Tangerang. A flood of water came into the village at terrific speed, rising to man's height. After a few minutes it streamed back into the sea, carrying with it people, animals, houses and trees. When he saw the water coming, Jacobs drove off in his cart as fast as he could. The flood overtook him, rising higher and higher. He stripped off his clothes in order to swim, and he jumped into the water. The receding wave pulled him along with such force that he was thrown into a tree with a painful bang. This was his salvation. He held on, clutched the tree and stayed at its top until the flood subsided.

Gronjin also was saved by a tree. Frans was saved in an even more remarkable manner. He could not swim and he sprawled in the flood, swallowing muddy sea water. He became exhausted. He saw death grinning him in the face. At that very moment a saving angel in the shape of the corpse of a cow bumped into him. He climbed on to it, to the indignation of some crows, who considered it their private territory, and floated away seaward. Realising that, if no other help arrived, he would find his death in the waves of the sea on his improvised raft, Frans remembered, he said later, the proverb "The higher the need, the nearer to God," and he prayed more fervently than he had ever done before. His prayer was not in vain; the cow drifted against a large tree, on which Frans climbed, and where he remained until the flood subsided.

The dramatic rescue of the three auctioneers had its comic side, observed the Algemeen *Dagblad,* in whose pages the story appeared. Gronjin, Jacobs and Frans walked into Tangerang stark naked. They were spotted by the assistant Resident, who called out, "Hey, Chinese, where do you come from?" "We ar-re . . . nearly . . . dea-dead," came the reply. Calling to the three "Adams," the assistant Resident recognised them as his own Civil Servants. The naked Dutchmen went to the house of the Chinese tailor to get some clothes. The tailor had three beautiful daughters, whom he had given a Christian education. When they saw the nude men they fled; the moral of the story being, apparently, that had they been brought up as children of Nature, they would have stayed.

The death roll at Tangerang was reckoned at 1,974 Javanese and forty-six Asiatics. The darkness at Serang commenced at 10.30 and by 11 the blackout was complete. Ten minutes later the telegraphist reported to Batavia that it was raining gravel. At 11.30 the line went dead. Muffled sounds only were heard and the air became deathly still. The houses, outside and within, were smothered in ash which covered everything, chairs, tables, books and papers, under a cementlike layer. The native population of the town, reported the controller, panicked; some fled, others stayed to plunder the empty houses. The looters had a free hand. Confusion was increased by the cries of people searching for lost children, some of whom were not found until after twenty-four hours had elapsed. All the forty-six inhabitants of the village of Karang Antoe, on the coast, died, and their bodies were found piled in one heap.

The shock wave that left Krakatoa at 10.02, and the sea wave that followed, took longer to reach Batavia, ninety-four miles from the volcano. An ominous stillness prevailed, the air was sluggish and the sky cloudy. The atmosphere was oppressive; not a leaf, not a blade of grass stirred. There was no news from the Straits; the telegraph beyond Serang, the capital of Bantam, remained silent. Towards ten o'clock dark clouds rode up from the west. In the streets twilight set in.

Krakatoa's great explosion was registered by the pressure gauge at the gasworks in Batavia between 10.11 and 10.20 a.m. The gauge was not sufficiently accurate to record the exact time of its arrival, which has been calculated as eight minutes after the explosion. The air pressure jerked the gasometer out of its well and the rough trace on the diagram shot off the paper after registering .225 inches of mercury. The gauge returned to normal at .058 inches at 10.50 a.m.

Shortly after 10.15, a heavy rain of ash began to fall, obscuring the sky, deepening it to Stygian blackness and blotting out the daylight. It became pitch dark at 11 a.m., so that people could not see objects held in their hands, and candles and gas lamps needed to be lighted. The strain on the gas reserves became too great and the lamps went out. Business was totally suspended. The news, received in the capital at this time, that the Chinese camp at Merak had been destroyed the night before did nothing to reassure the frightened Batavians. All sorts of conjectures were hazarded. What is happening in the Straits? was the question asked on all sides. It became bitterly cold, by tropical standards; the temperature dropping from 79 to 74 degrees Fahrenheit. Then suddenly there came news of a new evil. The sea was rising rapidly.

The sea wave took two hours and thirteen minutes to travel from Krakatoa to Batavia. At 11.30 a.m. the water began to rise rapidly. A big sea swept in at 12.15, inundating the shore and forcing the tide gauge above its limits. The water fell at 12.36 and returned again at 2.48, when the gauge again registered the maxium reading. This second wave, it has been calculated, left Krakatoa two hours and two minutes after the first great wave, and it was eighty miles distant from Batavia when the first wave struck. The gauge continued to register waves, still abnormal but diminishing in size, until 0.40 a.m. next morning. Eighteen separate waves were registered, following each other in a periodic cycle every two hours.

The Java *Bode* published its reporter's story of the scenes in Batavia that morning:

> To give some idea of the tidal waves which agitated the sea and rivers, we need only say that at Tanjang Priok, in particular, the water rose 10 feet within a few minutes, that it not only wholly overflowed a portion of Lower Batavia quite suddenly, but also bore fully laden proas ashore like straws. This phenomenon was repeated at 2 p.m. but not so violently. However great was the force exerted by this heavy flow, there came a moment, after it had raged its utmost, when the water in masses of immense height suddenly ebbing away vanished, and left the river beds and sea bottom awhile dry. Meanwhile the thick,

heavy, and oppressive atmosphere, charged with sulphurous fumes, began to clear up somewhat in spite of the cold. It became lighter, and by the increasing light people beheld a sight seldom certainly witnessed here in the course of centuries. The streets or rather the roads, the trees, and the houses were covered with a wholly white layer of ashes, and presented in the land of the sun a genuine Dutch winter scene. In the meantime, when, later in the day, the distant detonations had ceased and the rumbles had become fainter, no one had yet the least idea of the havoc wrought by this strange natural phenomenon.

The waves wrought great havoc in Batavia. An immense volume of water drove up the rivers, which were at their dry-monsoon state of lowness, throwing proas and small craft ashore. A few native fisherman were drowned and a Chinese village was destroyed; three hundred bodies were found and buried. At times the waves mounted three feet high on the town's quays. Dutchmen left their places of business downtown and hurried home to the New Town. Labourers struck work and made off in crowds. In the Chinese camp there was a great uproar, bustle and tumult, greater than usual, Batavians remarked. Every Chinaman sought a proa into which he could load his family and valuables, not realising, as their fellow citizens were not slow to remark, that they were entrusting themselves to a more formidable foe than the one they were seeking to escape. "No pen can depict the confusion in Old Batavia, resulting especially from the natives and Chinese seeking safety by general flight," wrote a reporter.

At Tanjang Priok, Batavia's port, the water rose ten feet in minutes, and the steamer *Princess Wilhelmina*, packed with women and children, was in the act of stranding. She was torn from her anchors and driven on shore, from where she was rescued by tugs. The tide rose twelve feet in the docks on Onrust Island, putting the great floating dock bearing the *Augusta*, a three-masted barque, in jeopardy. The heavy chains holding the dock snapped like glass and it collided with the Government steamer *Siak*, breaking her paddle wheel, and knocking down the funnel. Lieutenant G. F. Tydemann, on

board the warship *Koningin Emma der Nederlander,* provides
a somewhat incoherent but nonetheless exciting story of these
events:

By 9.30 a.m. it was too dark in the long room to do anything
so Goedhart and I tried to make the most of the diminishing
light by sitting by the rear, starboard, porthole reading. There
was just enough light for that. We had only been there a short
time when I felt a strange pressure in the ears. I had taken
quinine the night before to counteract the influence of Onrust,
but the effect of the quinine had never been like this. A temperature maybe, I thought, and went on reading. A while, perhaps
a quarter of an hour later, the same feeling of pressure came
again, and as I looked up as if to study this sensation, Goedhart
said, "What a strange feeling I have in my ears, as if something
was pressing. I had it just now as well." "Me too. It must be the
air pressure. Let's look at the barometer." Sure enough, this
showed a lessening of pressure, three millimetres [0.118 inches]
fall in a few minutes, then for half a minute steady, then again
fast rising of about seven millimetres [0.276 inches], again a
short lull, then again a fall, and so on for some time in succession. A feeling of pressure in the ears with the rise; relief with
the fall and a soft crackling noise. Gradually the times grew
longer and the swinging shorter. By twelve o'clock they were
no longer noticeable and the barometer remained quiet.
    Meanwhile the ash rain fell thicker and it became darker.
For something to do and because the barometer was behaving
so oddly, the Captain, Jonkheer von Schmidt auf Attenstadt,
ordered the yards and top-masts to be taken down. It was not
wind pressure but water pressure which was turning the vessel.
While the men were busy in the rigging, the water began to
rise fast, just before noon, so fast and so high that the provision
of the strongest mooring-rope was urgently necessary. Even
higher came the tide, soon washing over the top of the jetty.
Was it in fact water which rose? Was it not the bottom of the
sea, the island itself perhaps, which was sinking before our eyes,
perhaps for good?
    Who, seeing the water rise every minute and creeping towards
the houses, could answer that burning question? Who could

say whether this unlucky bit of ground would not shortly be only a few feet high, with all the houses sunk many feet deep. Minutes of anxious tension followed, almost of paralysis, but also of the selfish awareness that those who stood on the deck of a good ship were safe for the time being.

Lamps had been lighted an hour before on the Island. Everything looked drab and reddish through the peculiar mist. People stared vacantly, not knowing what to do. Others walked fast, backwards and forwards. Roofs and trees were grey as from never-seen snow. The floating dock with the three-master *Augusta* in it, an immovable threatening mass, loomed even larger than otherwise through the haze.

And suddenly, as the swelling of the water began to dawn on the inhabitants, there came cries of fear, at first far away and smothered, approaching and growing rapidly; a cry of distress from islanders and Chinese, mostly women and children who in panic tried to climb aboard anything that would float, into the sloops and on to the ships in the harbour, on to the Government steamer *Siak*, on to the floating dock, from which they were turned away, because its people had all they could do to keep the dock afloat, and finally also on board our ship.

A terror-stricken throng clambered aboard, causing terror thereto, where every moment we expected to see the mooring-ropes break, or the rails torn away. "Everyone aft. Everyone to the main deck," the officers ordered, trying to calm the terrified crowd. They had little difficulty in making room for the fear-driven people, till the ship was crowded to the half-deck. But they must hurry, for the ropes are taut like heart-strings.

One woman wishes to leave the ship. But the quarter-master, standing at the gangway, pushes her back, instinctively wishing to prevent her rushing to her doom. "My children, my children," she cries. She has lost two children in the crowd, as she was pushed forward by the mass of people surging behind her. But the quarter-master still pushes her back. Maybe he does not understand what she tearfully says, busy as he is with the stream of refugees. One officer has understood. "Let her go, quarter-master." Cynically but humanely he adds, "Let her drown with her children if she wants to." But it is already too late. As she tries to push against the crush on the gangway, the pressure decreases, but only because the gangways are on the point of falling, and seconds later they slip from the jetty and one is pushed forward by the water rushing past.

For what the shocked islanders had not seen had already been noticed on board; the water had reached its highest level and had already started to fall, turning against the direction of the flow. With the rise of a moderate flow of water from the west, the port-side anchor, lying in the fairway of the channel, had safeguarded us a safe anchorage. The launch and boat had already been smashed together, through the pressure of the ship against the jetty, so that the smaller boat was wrecked. The water outflowing towards the west gradually acquired a speed estimated at seven knots. Bow rope and back spring parted, the bow spring pulled, and the stern of the ship sheered off. The strong tide came at an angle, under the starboard side of the vessel, and stretched the stern ropes tight on that side.

Carefully all those nearby moved forward, staring in fearsome expectation of what would break or yield, the ship's sides or the bollards, chain or the anchors? The balance lasted thus, only a few seconds, while the ship lay rudderless under the terrible pressure. Then suddenly there was a tremendous sweep of the stern to the offside of the channel, towards the Kuiper Reef; a sweep so impressive that everyone who watched it subconsciously set his shoulder against the expected jolt. And it was if it was turned by an invisible hand for, without a jolt, the ship now lay motionless but notwithstanding the water from a much wider flow. Only one stern chain, the mushroom anchor chain, now held. The other, from the buoys, lay loose in folds. The mooring-post, dug into the channel and held by a 30-lb. weight, was torn out of the loosened coral base.

And now the bow chains were also ready to give; the mooring-posts were already floating. But just as they were about to sink, the order was heard, which so often gives seamen a feeling of temporary safety, "Stand by starboard anchor. Let out chain. Drop anchor."

Was the ship no longer bearing down on the Kuiper Reef, or had the mushroom anchor really found a favourable spot in which to fasten itself, just in time? The lead would perhaps provide the answer.

"Out with the lead to port." "Three and three-quarter fathoms," called the seaman. Five fathoms was the greatest depth. Surprisingly, the anchor had broken the strain. I could hardly believe it. But the lead sounding seemed doubtful on account of the strong current. Two minutes later our fears were calmed when a heavy downward drag on the chain caused the anchor to lose its grip. Three weeks later, when the vessel lay in dry dock, the zinc outer covering was found to be undamaged.

As terror rose in the hearts of the people as the water rose, so did it diminish with its retreat. For even the uneducated know that the first tidal wave is the biggest.

An hour later the sea reached its lowest level, some feet below the usual water-mark. The natives, who a few moments before had skirted death by drowning, jumped around the dried-out coral reefs, catching the silver white fish which, seemingly, had swum around the pools they knew never dried out, up until the last minute. Despairingly they searched for greater depths, thereby betraying their presence.

The warship now seemed safe, but a new danger loomed suddenly. Through the ash fog came the cry, "The dock is adrift." Tydemann watched the great floating dock crash against the *Siak*, twisting her paddle and cutting her mooring ropes, which split like beans from a pod. What was going to happen?

If the dock really broke entirely loose, there was no doubt the whole mass of dock and the three-master in it would be carried by the strong tide between Onrust and the Kuiper Reef, just where the *Emma* lay blocking the way. The massive dock would force a way through; and then anything might happen. For those who stood subconsciously measuring sizes and distance, it was clear enough that, if at best the dock should remain upright, our ship would be pinned against the harbour wall. The outcome remained a matter of conjecture, for the Harbour-Director, Captain Marinkelle, and the Crew-Master, Lieutenant Ledeboer, successfully held that awkward shape in its place and checked the danger.

The water rose and fell several times, flowing backwards and forwards, and diminishing slowly. Tydemann watched the

Blommendal, a surveying vessel, manned by a crew of ninety-six capsize. Four men were thrown in the water; two were saved. The *Volharding* and the floating dock also broke loose and drifted seawards. "The ash rain," says Tydemann, "started to diminish about 3 p.m., and the light returned slightly."

Verbeek paced his garden all day. It was so dark in Buitenzorg at 10.15 a.m. that house and carriage lamps needed to be lighted. Fifteen minutes later, the geologist saw at the far end of his garden a freakish, thick yellow cloud, which rolled down to earth, standing out clearly from the surrounding air, like chimney smoke. He ran to the end of his garden, hoping to pick up particles of pumice but, to his surprise, all he found was water vapour, devoid of any smell. Verbeek remarked no special explosion that morning, but at 11.20 a.m. there started a rain of ash which continued until 1.00 p.m., and carried on intermittently until the middle of the afternoon. It contained, he discovered, small round grains which crushed to flourlike grey powder between his fingers.

Krakatoa's final roar came at 10.52 a.m., and eight minutes later the gas-pressure gauge at Batavia registered .165 inches of mercury. At that moment, it is thought, the remnant of the cone of Danan collapsed into the chasm formed fifty minutes earlier by the greater cataclysm. No great wave followed, and this was the end of the volcano's eruption. The aftereffects continued for many hours.

9. Plenty Lives Lost

THE RAGING DEMON has slunk back to his prison cell, deep beneath the island he has torn to pieces. It will stay down there for ten thousand years, perhaps, before it again struggles to be free.

It is still pitch dark in the Straits. The dead are gone beyond recall. The living struggle to survive. For all they know, they are the only people left alive.

Save the *Berouw,* the *Marie,* and the *Siak,* no big ship in or near the Straits suffered damage either from the outfall of the eruption or from the sea waves. No vessel was more fortunate than the *Charles Bal.* She sailed through the jaws of death, into the mouth of hell. During the twenty-two hours the eruption lasted, she was never more than thirty miles from Krakatoa, and during Sunday night she passed within twelve miles of the roaring volcano. She rode the great wave which passed beneath her, unobservable in that depth of water. Blessing his good fortune, Captain Watson on Monday afternoon pushed on through the Straits. The mud rain ceased at 2 p.m. and there was sufficient light to see the yards aloft. At 5 p.m. he could discern the horizon to the north, but the sky hung dark and heavy until midnight, when he logged his ship's position as sixty-five miles southeast of Noordwatcher Island, just outside the Straits. His ship, from truck to waterline, looked as if it had been cemented, and the spars, sails, blocks and ropes were in a terrible mess. How fared it with Anjer, Merak, and the little villages on the Java coast? Watson wondered.

Telegraph Master Schruit, we recall, after making his escape from Anjer, sought his way back, reaching a village about 10 a.m. The party of refugees rested for several hours, sitting in a circle, unable to sleep. About 5 p.m., Schruit walked further in the direction of the coast, arriving at a small mosque where he found Mme. Schuit and several other survivors from Anjer. The priest "uttered no word of reproach" at this desecration by Christians. Indeed, an obliging native brought the Dutch cigarettes which they lighted gladly. The women received Schruit with great joy, each telling him their escape story. While the village headman cooked food, Schruit despatched a native to reconnoitre. He returned to report that there was no longer such a place as Anjer, and that the site of the town was unapproachable. He advised Schruit not to try to reach it, but rather to climb a nearby hill from where the scene was visible.

Let Schruit tell his story:

> We then started, Madame Schuit accompanied us, and we soon reached the hill. The site where Anjer had once stood was before us, but every vestige of it was level with the ground; not a tree, not a house, nothing was there left. The sight was fearful, and the impression it made on the refugees was most sad.
>
> We therefore decided to turn our backs on the site of Anjer, and took our way along a road all but impassable from fallen trees, broken branches, and the showers of mud. This road led to Gointoen. We got there about ten o'clock, and were again supplied with food; there was not much, but it was a great relief to us. At eleven o'clock Doctor Dillié with his family arrived, and as the ladies were too much fatigued to go any further, it was decided that only the men should undertake the journey to Mantjah.
>
> About half-a-mile from that place we met the horses which the Resident had sent for our use, and close to Mantjah we found the Resident himself and his suite. At Mantjah, there were some other refugees, and among them Madame B., and after being refreshed with a draught of wine we went on to Tjelegon, and remained there till eight o'clock the following morning, when we began the journey to Serang. After a few more mischances and great fatigue we arrived there. I was

kindly entertained by the Controller, and began slowly to re-
cover from the fatigues I had undergone, thankful indeed to
the Almighty that my life had been spared.

The *Loudon*, steaming from Telok Betong for Anjer, reached
the Java coast on the morning of the 29th, the first ship to sail
across the Straits after the eruption.

Captain Lindemann, anxious as he was to leave Telok
Betong, found the darkness too great to sail from Lampong
Bay before 4 a.m. on August 28th. By daybreak, the *Loudon*
was steaming slowly down the Sumatra coastline, making for
the channel between Sebokoe Island and the mainland, through
which Lindemann expected to make his way to Anjer. When
the *Loudon* was still two miles away, Lindemann saw that "a
connection had been formed between the island and the mainland." Floating pumice blocked the channel. Lindemann sought
a passage between Sebokoe and Sebassi; that channel was also
completely blocked. Lindemann steamed back up Lampong
Bay, seeking a passage through the Straits of Lagoendi on the
western side of the bay. Even there the way was barred by a
large expanse of pumice. He determined to force a passage.
Slowly the *Loudon* pushed through the obstruction. As the
vessel forged ahead, the layer of pumice parted, piling up at
her bows and disclosing its depth as ten feet. It took the
Loudon ten minutes to get clear and into open water. Lindemann set his course for Krakatoa, and he sent the boatswain
to the foreyard to keep lookout. Lindemann and van Sandick
stood on the bridge, wondering what they would see.

The *Loudon* sailed close to Krakatoa on the morning of
August 29th. Lindemann is brief in his description of the volcano: "As we steamed past Krakatoa, we noticed that the middle of the island had disappeared. However, when we got to
the east of the island, we discovered that between it and
Sebessi a reef had formed, and various craters planted on it
were now and then sending up columns of smoke on high."

Fortunately van Sandick is more expansive in his pen picture
of the island shortly after the great eruptions:

Arriving before the island of Krakatoa, there is not any doubt that this is the cursed volcano which is the cause of all the misfortune, because the crater which distributed so much smoke and ash two days previously is destroyed, and the waves of the sea pass peacefully where there had been dry land. No more than one-quarter of the island can be seen, and the part swallowed up was as though torn, over an expanse of 25 sq. kilometres [approximately 9½ square miles], from the remaining section. Only two reefs, terrible sights, now rose above the vanished area. The volcanic eruption had not completely ceased. At eight different points thick columns of smoke could be seen, the centres of which were black and the exteriors entirely white. These columns rose and disappeared at very frequent intervals.

Three-quarters of Krakatoa Island had disappeared. The cone of Rakata had been split in two, leaving a sheer cliff on its northern face. Where, two days previously, the island had measured eighteen square miles, now only eleven square miles of surface remained. The rest of the island, one and one-eighth cubic miles of matter, had gone, no one then knew where. The islet of Polish Hat had ceased to exist; both Lang and Verlaten islands were greatly enlarged, and two new banks now rose from the sea bed.

The *Loudon* steamed on towards the Javanese coast. "When she neared the shore, we observed that here, too, everything had been laid waste," recounts Captain Lindemann. Nothing but a small stump remained of the lighthouse at Fourth Point, he noticed, and of Anjer there was nothing to be seen. Van Sandick was more observant:

A horrifying spectacle presented itself to our eyes; the coasts of Java, as those of Sumatra, were entirely destroyed. Everywhere the same grey and gloomy colour prevailed. The villages and trees had disappeared; we could not even see any ruins, for the waves had demolished and swallowed up the inhabitants, their homes, and their plantations. We had difficulty recognising Anjer, as not one house of this lively town was left standing. This was truly a scene of the Last Judgment.

Van Sandick heard a noise behind him. Turning back, he saw the coolies, whom the vessel had taken from Anjer, looking at their town, its rice fields destroyed, its houses gone, a muddy bog where no living thing remained, the place where they had left their wives and children. "These poor people must be extremely unhappy," thought Sandick, imagining they would want to disembark at once to search for their families. Not at all, he found, "for without any feelings of regret for their ruined homes, for their families and friends, they suddenly began to dance around, expressing their joy at having so happily escaped the disaster."

The *Loudon* dropped anchor at 4 p.m., at the spot where Anjer had stood four days before. Lindemann and van Sandick went ashore to see what information could be obtained. There they met the Resident of Bantam, Heer van Spaan, who told them the extent of the disaster. From this information van Sandick deduced, as he stated in his newspaper story, that the total number of persons who had perished in Java and Sumatra exceeded forty million. Millions of corpses lay in one burial place alone, he assured his readers in Holland. The *Loudon* left Anjer Roads at ten minutes to five o'clock, at the request of the Resident, who asked to be taken to Bantam Bay.

Several survivors were struggling to reach safety on the hills behind Anjer. Pilot de Vries on Monday afternoon reached Serang, where he was received into the house of a Mr. Metman. Here he was able to take the rest he sorely needed, and to change his clothes, which were in tatters and covered with pumice. A doctor, called by the hospitable Mr. Metman, ordered de Vries to a hospital, where he recovered from his wounds. The Englishman at Chikandie Udik remained in his house until the afternoon of Monday, when the sky began to clear. Although he had kept doors and windows closed, the ash and dust found its way inside, spoiling the food, clogging everything, and filling his eyes. Normal daylight did not return for three days, he states.

The Rev. Tennyson-Woods gathered some information on his visit to the disaster area three weeks later:

The few who escaped to the high lands remained in the villages on the hillsides, fearing to return to the lower ground lest other tidal waves should engulf them. It was said that the natives manifested great animosity towards the Europeans, and blamed them as being the cause of this calamity. "This," they said, "is a judgment for your cruelty towards the Achimese." I doubt very much, however, if this was a feeling that was very general. The poor natives seem to have behaved with the utmost patience under the awful misfortunes which came so unexpectedly upon them. Their means of living were suddenly taken from them. Crops, cattle, homes, and families were destroyed, and famine seemed inevitably before them. If, in the first instincts of self-preservation, they looked out for themselves, refusing aid to an alien and not very popular race, it would be no wonder. Yet very few such instances are recorded. One Dutch lady states that she was refused a drink of water except in exchange for a gold ring. On the other hand, one of the survivors stated to me that when he made his way to a village (Tjemangoe) clad only in a ragged sarong, the people took him in and gave him both clothes and food, and seemed to forget their own misfortunes in attending to his. Food of course was very scarce, and unless prompt aid had been rendered by the Government, no doubt many of those who crowded into the upland villages would have died of starvation.

Engineer Nieuwenhys reached Merak on his return from Batavia early on Tuesday morning. He found all his friends, except Peckler, dead, and the town in ruins. In the quarries, locomotives had been carried fifteen hundred yards from their sheds and lay dinted as if they were made of tin; cranes had been swept away; and iron rails had been twisted together like ribbons. He saw bodies floating in the sea, and several were thrown on the beach. He dug hasty graves for the bodies of two of his friends. On his way back to the hill he met Peckler and listened to his confused story.

Early on Tuesday, the Governor-General of the Dutch East Indies sent steamers to the scene of the disaster. The *Kederie* sailed for the Lampongs.

We left Mrs. Beyerinck leaning against a tree. She had fled

Krakatoa during the early stage of eruption. From a photograph taken on May 27, 1883, by M. Hamburg, a passenger aboard the *Loudon*. (Credit: The Royal Society)

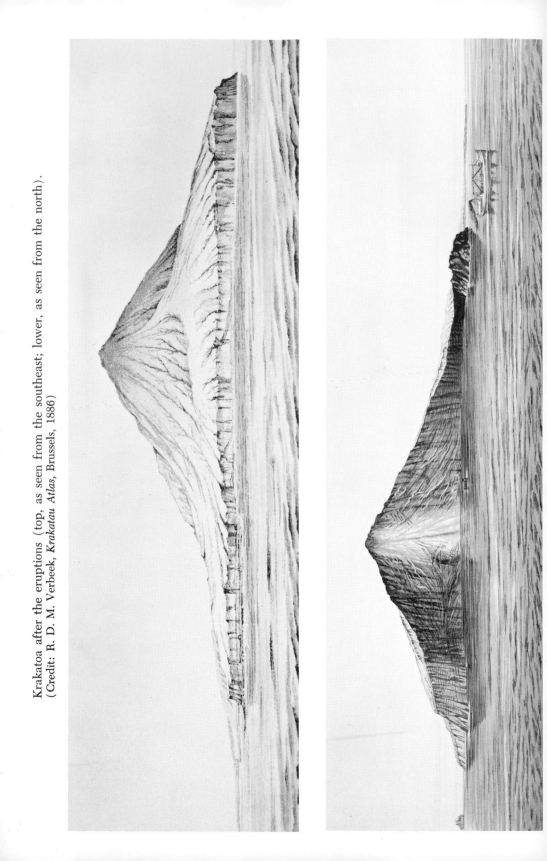

Krakatoa after the eruptions (top, as seen from the southeast; lower, as seen from the north). (Credit: R. D. M. Verbeek, *Krakatau Atlas*, Brussels, 1886)

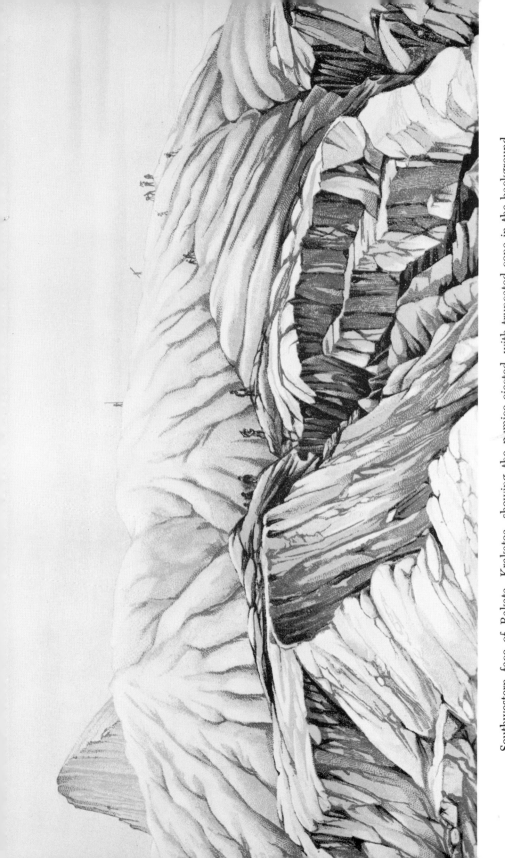

Southwestern face of Rakata, Krakatoa, showing the pumice ejected, with truncated cone in the background. (Credit: *Krakatau Atlas*)

View of Krakatoa from the islet of Calmeijer within a few weeks of the eruption.
(Credit: *Krakatau Atlas*)

The cliff face of Rakata (the peak of Krakatoa) as left after three-quarters of the island had been engulfed.
(Credit: C. E. Stehn)

Rakata, west coast showing the cliffs of pumice built up during the eruption. This photograph offers some idea of the immense amount of material ejected, more than 100 feet thick in places.
(Credit: C. E. Stehn)

Birth of Anak ("child of") Krakatoa. The following six photos were taken at intervals of six seconds, on January 24, 1928, from Verlaten Island.
(Credit: C. E. Stehn)

Anak Krakatoa, 1928 (above) and 1929 (below), the emergence of the crater cone. (Credit: C. E. Stehn)

Chart illustrating the positions of the towns and tracks of vessels where the most important observations bearing on the great final outburst of Krakatoa were made. The black coastal areas are those which were submerged during the great sea waves.
(Credit: *Krakatoa* [Royal Society, London, 1888]).

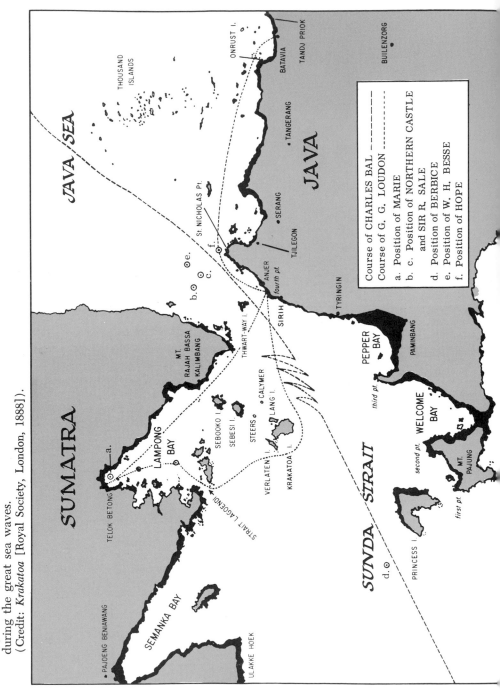

Aerial view of Anak Krakatoa in June, 1959. Rakata, the large island remnant from the 1883 eruption, is in the background.
(Credit: R. W. Decker)

Aerial view of Anak Krakatoa showing the off-center shape of the crater, June, 1959.
(Credit: R. W. Decker)

Anak Krakatoa in January, 1960. Rakata Island is in the background. The height of the eruption clouds can be estimated from the 500-foot high silhouette of Anak Krakatoa. (Credit: R. W. Decker)

Seismograph tent on Anak Krakatoa. Explosion vibrations originated at 600 feet below sea level and were recorded several seconds before the eruption explosions from the crater.
(Credit: R. W. Decker)

Three thousand-foot mushroom of volcanic gas and ash from Anak Krakatoa, January, 1960. The explosive energy in this eruption is equivalent to 170 tons of T.N.T. (Credit: R. W. Decker)

The larger explosive eruptions of Anak Krakatoa throw large blocks of hot but solid lava well beyond the crater rim. Small dust sprays mark their impact. (Credit: R. W. Decker)

Two men can stand in the small impact crater of the explosively ejected blocks thrown up to 2,000 feet from the vent area. .
(Credit: R. W. Decker)

The inner cinder cone and crater of Anak Krakatoa are displacing a former crater lake. The new cone's rim is 300 feet in diameter (January, 1960).
(Credit: R. W. Decker)

from the hut four hundred feet up on the slopes of Mount
Radjah Bassa, in which she and her family had taken shelter.
The skin of her hands is hanging in shreds. She has been terribly burnt by the rain of hot pumice and ash which descended
on Sumatra shortly after the great explosion on Monday at
10.02 a.m. Several hours have elapsed, and it is now dead calm.
She can hear nothing, no human or animal, and she thinks she
must be dead, and on the path to heaven or hell:

Was it imagination or did I hear something after all? I listened and heard, first dampened and then more clearly, someone shouting and screaming for me. Everything was once more
clear in my mind.

I recognised my husband's voice calling me and shouting.
Why was I dead and all the rest of them still alive. I heard
Tojaka (the clerk) say to him, "Master, be calm, the children
are still alive." I tried to shout, and at last succeeded in calling, "I am alive." Tojaka was the first to hear me. "Master, I hear
your wife." I shouted loud and long, "I'm coming. I'm coming."

I couldn't find the way back, and ran in the opposite direction. But when I realised that my husband's voice got further
and further away, I turned round again. Had I gone any further,
I would have fallen into a ravine, we discovered later.

Controller Beyerinck carried his wife to the hut. "Let us
stay here and die together," he cried. "No, we shall be rescued
and taken to hospital in Batavia," she answered, hearing the
sound of her own voice as if another person spoke. "Who knows
whether Batavia still exists," Mr. Beyerinck told her.

Of the three thousand natives who clustered around the hut,
one thousand died of burns, and the skins of those who survived were blistered and burned. The body of one man was
found weeks later sprawled in a sheet of pumice, his arms
spread, his legs askew, just as he fell in panic-stricken flight.
Only in southeastern Sumatra did Krakatoa itself claim victims,
by its burning ash and red-hot pumice; elsewhere it was the
waves that killed.

Mrs. Beyerinck sat on the ground by the hut. The ayah gave

her the youngest child. From the way his mouth was working, she could see he must be terribly thirsty. She tried to give him her breast, but suddenly the child lay still in her arms. She felt him all over and laid her ear to his heart. She could hear nothing. "Thank God this child is at least put out of his agony," she told the ayah, who cried bitterly; but Mrs. Beyerinck could not shed a tear. It would have been a great relief to cry, but she could not. "Wrap the child in a blanket and lay it on the bed," she tried to say, but the frightful thirst caused by the hot ash dried the words in her throat. Let Mrs. Beyerinck tell her own story:

There was still deep darkness. We couldn't light a fire, as matches went out immediately. At last the head boy, the only remaining male servant, managed to start a small fire, and we began to hear signs of life from the people in the village, some of whom came to the light, asking for water. They were crazy from thirst and anxiety, so that it began to be dangerous for us. My husband said, "I have no weapons, but there is an axe behind the bed." The house-boy fetched it. When my husband held it he said, "I cannot do anything with it. I have lost the use of my hand." "Then give it to me," I said and clutched the axe. I was suddenly furious that my children's lives depended on it. I would have cut down the first person to stand in my way. When three men came towards the hut, the house-boy advised us to put out the fire, as one of them was carrying a kris. We quickly threw ash on the fire and again we were in darkness. I don't know how long we had been sitting when we saw people approaching, carrying torches. There must have been thirty of them. They shouted, "Sir, if you are still alive, come with us. We must leave because soon there will be more fire." "From whence?" asked my husband. "From Radjah Bassa, look," they cried. We looked up and saw a ray of greenish light on the mountain. "Wait for us; we'll get ready," my husband answered.

Once again the Beyerincks turned to flee, in the mistaken belief that the old volcano on the slopes of which they were sheltering was about to join Krakatoa in eruption. Mrs. Beyerinck saw that none of the female servants had enough strength left to carry her four-year-old son, so she had him strapped to her back with his legs dangling over her hips. Her husband led their daughter by the hand. The girl's hands and face were badly burned. The refugees descended the mountain and set off across the paddy fields below. It took them fifteen minutes to reach the woods. The path had vanished. Even the largest trees had fallen. Mrs. Beyerinck understood in what terrible danger she had been earlier. When she ran from the hut, she had become entangled in the roots of an enormous tree. On the ground she noticed the footsteps she had left; hanging on the trees were shreds from her sarong. Now, an enormous tree lay across the spot where she had stood.

Mrs. Beyerinck couldn't walk another step; the child was very heavy. Some people came up. They had survived the ash rain by bathing in a river. All their houses had collapsed, and most of the inhabitants of the district had been killed, they told the controller. It started to rain again, no longer ash, but hot, heavy mud. The Beyerincks did not dare return to their hut, because so many dead lay there. She sent a servant back instead, to bring down a large table, under which she placed the children. She and her husband lay on either side to protect them. All this was done, she says, by the light from a tiny flame made by the house boy from a piece of felt-roofing. She sent him to fetch water from the river. He returned to report it was not fit to drink. It was all muddy. "Perhaps it may be better in a couple of hours," he said, when the water from the well on the mountain cleared it. So it proved, but the water was still covered with ash. It quenched their thirsts, but the "more we drank, the thirstier we got," found Mrs. Beyerinck. Luckily she had still the bottle of orange syrup, and she mixed it with the water, giving everyone a drink from time to time. Her husband and Mr. Tojaka approved of everything she did. Mrs. Beyerinck prayed to God to be saved; if they were to die, she asked that they should not have to suffer too much. But a small voice within her seemed to whisper, "You will be saved, you and those you love."

It seemed centuries that they sat in complete darkness. Sometimes Mrs. Beyerinck slept, overcome with exhaustion. She awoke into frightened consciousness. She was afraid for her small son. He drank when she held the cup to his mouth, but otherwise he showed no sign of life. Her daughter Mientze clung to her, crying, "Mummy, don't go. Stay with Mientze." Suddenly Mr. Beyerinck clutched her arm and pointed to the sky. Mrs. Beyerinck saw a small patch of light. "It is the moon," cried her husband. The light grew and brightened, until it became clear moonlight.

Mrs. Beyerinck describes this great moment:

> On standing up, which was very difficult, I noticed that my limbs were swollen to three times their normal size. No one spoke. We all held our breath for, after such a long darkness, we yearned for God's heavenly sun or moonlight. The circle of light gradually became blood-red. The strong wind tore apart the mass of ash, and we saw the wonderful, glittering sunlight.

Mrs. Beyerinck does not explain what day it was, and we can conclude only that it is by now the morning of Thursday, August 30th, for the blackness did not disperse until then.

Mr. Beyerinck got busy. He promised two unwounded natives, "I will richly reward each one of you if you will each take a child of mine on your back and follow me." The men did so and Mr. Beyerinck told his wife and Mr. Tojaka to follow him. "There are too many bodies here. Let us get away," he ordered. Mrs. Beyerinck stood with her face turned to the sun, her eyes closed, and she prayed for further protection, thanking God for the sunlight. When she opened her eyes she saw that she and Tojaka stood alone. Her husband and the men carrying the children were far ahead. Looking at the clerk, she noticed with surprise that he turned his head away. When she asked why he would not look at her, he seized her, his whole body trembling. Poor man, she noticed, he was nearly blinded and his body was terribly burnt. Looking at her at last, he said in a secretive way, "I saw that face of yours in my dreams a week ago." At first Mrs. Beyerinck did not understand what he meant. She guessed, when she put her hands to her face; the skin was hanging in shreds.

She and Mr. Tojaka caught up with Mr. Beyerinck. It was light enough to see for some distance. She could see across the Straits. "Where was Krakatoa?" she wondered. She could see only half of the large cone; the smaller cones were gone. Where six days before they had risen into the sky, eight little islands had sprung up, and from each smoke arose. Near at hand she saw that all the villages by the beach had gone. On the sea floated a wide belt of pumice. On it lay roofs of houses, fallen trees, their branches snapped, and dark shapes which she could not at first identify, and which she learned later were the bodies of men and animals.

"Come," called her husband. Mrs. Beyerinck looked back towards the hut where her youngest child lay dead. "We cannot even bury him," she thought. "Come, come, we must leave," Mr. Beyerinck told her. She could not move. She saw that she was more or less naked. Her sarong was gone; her hair hung loose. When she tried to put it up, her hands hurt. She could not tie her hair into a bun any more. Her legs were bleeding, their skin raw. She held ash against the wounds to stop the blood flowing.

Mrs. Beyerinck hobbled on for half an hour, leaning on Mr. Tojaka. "I can't go any further, let me lie here," he moaned. Mrs. Beyerinck tried to help him. "Go," he told her, "you will be lost if you stay here. The wind will bury you in ash." Supporting her husband's clerk, Mrs. Beyerinck staggered on. They reached a ditch in which a man was crouching. "Help, help," he shouted. "I've got cholera." "Give me a glass of brandy, in the name of Allah," he beseeched, "then I shall be cured." Mrs. Beyerinck said she could not help him, and she and Mr. Tojaka went on.

The sun was now at its zenith. The heat was terrible. Mrs. Beyerinck felt she was going to collapse. Her hair stifled her.

It was heavy with ash. "If I don't get rid of my hair, I shall become unconscious," she told Mr. Tojaka. A native came up. He had a knife in his hand. She asked him to cut off her hair. He agreed and told her to lie on a fallen tree trunk, which she did. Mr. Tojaka turned his head away. He told Mrs. Beyerinck later that he thought the man was going to cut off her head. The man cut her hair, shook the ash from it, and offered it to her. Mrs. Beyerinck told him to throw it away.

She and the clerk walked on, reaching a road on which the ash had been beaten flat by countless feet. Others were alive, too, the marks told Mrs. Beyerinck. "If we rest here," she told Mr. Tojaka, "they will be able to find us." They sat by the road for hours. Her husband sent some people to search for them. They found Mrs. Beyerinck and the clerk and took them to a half-demolished house, the only one still standing in the village, where she saw her husband and the two children lying in deep sleep. Night fell. Mrs. Beyerinck watched the stars, then she too fell asleep.

Next morning, an old man, whom she had known since childhood, brought Mrs. Beyerinck some cooked chicken and a bowl of rice. The rice was covered with ash, but it was nonetheless welcome. She called her husband. He made a grunt, but the children did not react at all. "Heavens, are they dead?" she wondered. She tried to walk to them, but she could not stand up, so she rolled over and touched them. "They were alive but senseless, from hunger probably," she thought. She tore the chicken apart in her wounded hands and put a piece in the mouth of each child. The boy had not strength enough to chew, although he made movements as if he wanted to eat. Mrs. Beyerinck chewed the piece of chicken to soften it, and put it into the child's mouth again. The boy sucked and swallowed it. She did the same for her husband and her daughter, and slowly they regained consciousness. She gave them each a drink. When they were better, Mrs. Beyerinck asked the old man whether he could find her a piece of paper and a pencil. "I will ask the commissioner to send someone to fetch us. We can't stay here. Our wounds are beginning to stink," she told him. He found a dirty piece of paper, on which Mrs. Beyerinck scribbled a desperate entreaty. She asked the old man to find someone to carry it through the desert of ash to Telok Betong. The commissioner, she learned later, received the note, but nothing was done. Mrs. Beyerinck says that he was an un-feeling man who had lost his head, and he was pensioned off for not helping her and her family—an unfair criticism, no doubt, for the people in Telok Betong were in desperate straits themselves.

Mrs. Beyerinck sent the old native to the beach to signal passing ships. After endless waiting night fell again. Next morning, her cook's daughter came. "Where are your mother and sister?" asked Mrs. Beyerinck. "They are all dead," an-swered the girl. "I buried them in the ash. All your other servants, including Jeroemoedi, are dead too."

Some hours went by; then a man came running from the beach to report: "There is a boat but it is sailing past." Mrs. Beyerinck prayed and prayed, so long and so loudly that her husband begged her to desist. "It makes me nervous," he told her. "The boat is at anchor," reported another running native. Looking towards the beach Mrs. Beyerinck saw a man coming. He was dressed in white and wore a cork hat. He was small of stature and walked with a roll, like a sailor.

The sailor was Captain Hoen, the commander of the *Kederie*. For four days the barge had sought a passage through the float-ing punice. The coast from Kalimbang to Telok Betong was completely cut off. Everywhere, Hoen could see, the country was devastated and covered with ash. At last, on Saturday, September 1st, a current forced a gap in the pumice and he was able to send a boat ashore near the village of Kali Antoe. In the only house still standing he found the controller of Kalimbang and his family.

They were in a deplorable condition, Captain Hoen saw at once, all covered with burns. "How can I get them to hospital alive," he wondered. "Bring litters," he ordered the natives who were standing by. When they seemed to hesitate, he warned them that if they did not help, no one would come out alive. The poor natives said they were without food and would starve, whereupon Hoen promised six bags of rice and three kilos of salt if they would help. While the litters were being hastily constructed from fallen bamboo stems, Captain Hoen talked with the Beyerincks. Mrs. Beyerinck was nearly naked, and he covered her with his coat. He lifted her gently, as if she was a child, and whispered in her ear, "I won't hurt you. Let me drown if I don't see you reach Batavia safely." Mrs. Beyerinck heard her husband say, "If my wife hadn't been here, we should all have been dead. She was our hope." "No, that is not true," Mrs. Beyerinck managed to say. "Everyone clings to life."

Mr. Beyerinck tried to tell the captain about the disaster.

> No human tongue could tell what happened. I think hell is the only word applicable to what we saw and went through. I am sure I was burnt mainly by fire that spurted out of the ground as we went along. At first, thinking only of the glowing ash showers, we endeavoured to shelter ourselves under beds, taking the risk of the house falling in, which no doubt it did on a great many, but the hot ashes came up through the crevices of the floor, and burned us still more.

Hundreds of corpses lay in the hills, the controller told Captain Hoen when he remarked that there were a few dead bodies by the shore.

Mr. Beyerinck was convinced that, as well as Krakatoa, Radjah Bassa had been in eruption, from vents on its slopes; a mistaken impression, as Geologist Verbeek discovered later when he investigated the assertion, which arose, probably, from the sight of the hot springs that existed on the mountain's flanks.

Beyerinck told Captain Hoen his wife had sent messages the forty-eight miles to Telok Betong for help, but no help had come. Just then a native headman reached the house; he had come over the hills from Telok Betong. The port had been wholly devastated, he announced. Only Mr. Altheers, the Resident, had been rescued. The town's other inhabitants lay buried under the ash. A wild exaggeration, as it turned out, for the majority of Europeans in the town survived the disaster.

The bearers carried the controller, Mrs. Beyerinck, and the two surviving children, both of whom were badly burned, down the steep mountain road. Captain Hoen walked by their side, trying to protect the invalids from the scorching sun with a large umbrella. They proved a difficult task as the path was obstructed by fallen trees which caused him to stumble, exposing their gaping wounds to the fierce sunlight. At one place, a hollow filled by sea water left by the waves, the bearers waded up to their chests. Mrs. Beyerinck could not help smiling when she heard Captain Hoen cursing the natives, half in Dutch and half in Malay, as they slipped and slithered. The journey to the beach took two hours, and the Beyerincks were more dead than alive at its end.

When the party reached the barge, or the sloop as Mrs. Beyerinck calls it, Captain Hoen enquired if she was in pain. "No, I'm terribly hungry," she replied. "You shall have the best we have on board," the Captain told her. She asked what day it was. To her horror, he replied it was Saturday. "How was it possible?" she wondered. She and her family had been in hellish darkness for four nights and three days. The eruption had started a week before. Captain Hoen put Mrs. Beyerinck in his own bunk, and gave her a glass of wine, which tasted like nectar, and some chicken soup. The good man, she says, fed her like a child. He told her not to worry, as her children were safe. Kalimbang, he said, had been totally destroyed by the big wave which was estimated to have reached one hundred feet high. The natives said it came over the palm trees. Two-thirds of the population of Controller Beyerinck's district had perished. The *Kederie* had tried to reach Telok Betong, stated Captain Hoen, but the vessel had been unable to get through the pumice that blocked the bay. He sailed along the coast, looking for a place to land. He had nearly passed the village when he saw people waving cocoanut palms and rags. When he rowed ashore, the natives told him of the Beyerincks' plight.

Before the *Kederie* sailed, the controller begged Captain
Hoen to give all the food he could spare to the villagers, who
were trying to reach the vessel through the lane in the pumice
made from the shore by the ship's boat. Hoen handed down
several bags of rice.

The Beyerincks and their faithful clerk were taken to a hospital in Batavia, where they recovered. Mrs. Beyerinck ends
her story with these words: "It was a miracle. However cruel
nature may be, and however mysterious God's ways, he didst
save us. His name be praised."

When Captain Hoen, prior to his rescue of the Beyerincks,
reached Telok Betong, the *Kederie* could not approach the
quay as the layer of pumice was thirty feet thick. The refugees
on Residency Hill watched in despair as the ship turned away.
At least 2,600 natives had been drowned. One European survivor, a man who had escaped to a nearby village on Monday,
describes his return to the stricken town:

> The sun did not show itself again until Tuesday morning.
> What a scene was then beheld. Everything was covered with a
> layer of ashes and mud one foot deep. When I again found my-
> self at Telok Betong and came near the Residency, I was over-
> powered by horror. At the foot of the hill on which that house
> stands lay a plain bare and laid waste. Nothing is left of Telok
> Betong and the surrounding villages. A few natives only could
> be seen on the plain, trying to salvage some of their furniture.
> But it was in vain; the sea had carried everything away save
> corpses and the Government iron cash boxes. Amongst the
> corpses were those of four Europeans, namely two sailors and
> two soldiers. One sailing vessel laden with salt held to her
> anchors and now rides securely in deep water. The misery is
> great. Our buffaloes, cattle, and horses have nothing to eat.
> Deer and wild pigs even come into the villages in search of
> food. Rice is short, and there is a lack of drinking water. All
> the available water tastes of sulphur and is muddy.

The salt-trader to which this man refers, was, of course, the
Marie. When daylight returned Mate Stokhluysen saw that,
of all the boats sheltering in the roadstead, only the *Marie* had

survived. Miraculously, the last wave had carried her off the beach, on which she had been stranded, and she now floated in deep water. Four of his crew had been drowned.

The anonymous survivor who wrote in the Java *Bode* has this to tell us about the days at Telok Betong following the disaster. His story recommences on Tuesday morning, the day after the big wave chased him up the hill:

> In tense anxiety of what to expect, we sat awaiting morning, when the terrible news came that the water had previously risen as high as the floor of the Government buildings, so everyone realised they had lost everything. But nobody could believe that. It was simply unbelievable. So, with torches, people went to the scene of the disaster to investigate. The terrible news proved only too true. The floating wood, which had been carried as high as the Residency, was the surest sign that it was no use to hope for the impossible. So it was decided to wait till the daylight, which should prove that everything was lost and one would have to start life all over again.
>
> At last morning came. In front of us was what was once a town, but there was no destruction. There was simply . . . nothing. Everything seemed to have vanished into the sea, except, as by pure magic, all the corpses, just as if to show us how many casualties the disaster had caused. Under those circumstances, however, there wasn't much time to moan. The corpses had to be buried to prevent epidemics, which would have caused an even greater disaster. The damage and the total number of casualties was impossible to guess. There we stood, having lost everything, not knowing where aid would come from. Luckily we could rely on the Resident and his wife, who gave us all shelter in their house, and the meals looked like the food of kings, under our circumstances.
>
> At this moment we are already their guests for a fortnight, and how many more days are there to come?

The refugees at Telok Betong had to await rescue until September 16th. Even then the Government ship had difficulty in getting through the layers of pumice which blocked the bay. When this man was taken off by rowing-boat, he gazed back at the place where he had lived. "Telok Betong is a silent grave, to be looked at from a distance, but not to be approached," he wrote.

Controller Le Soeur and other Dutch survivors were rescued from Samanka Bay and taken to Batavia.

When the eruption came to an end on Monday, the *W. H. Besse* groped her way through the Straits, like a ghost ship, thought her commander, Captain Baker. At 4 p.m. the wind moderated, "the explosions ceased, showers of ash not so heavy, able to see our way around the decks," he noted in his log. The vessel was covered with pumice and ash, which stuck to the rigging like glue. Weeks elapsed before it was all removed. One seaman who fell off the slippery forward hatch, died after the ship reached Boston, recorded Baker at the end of the voyage. On Tuesday the weather was calmer and at 8 p.m. the *W. H. Besse* reached the place where Anjer had stood. She sailed on slowly, rounding Java Head on August 31st, and moved out across the Indian Ocean, where she forged her way through thick banks of pumice, her captain declaring that after what his ship had gone through he was not afraid of any weather whatever on board her.

Both Captain Sampson of the *Norham Castle* and Captain Woolbridge of the *Sir Robert Sale* kept their ships outside the Straits for several days. They were able to make their way together, and pass through the Straits on August 28th; the seas, they reported, were filled with floating debris and the bodies of men and animals. Captain Woolbridge supplies us with a brief description of the last hours of black Monday. "At sunset the heavens presented a very terrible appearance, the dense mass of clouds covered with blood-red appearance, the sunbeams being seen through the volumes of cloud discharging from Krakatoa."

Seaman Dalby on the *Hope* watched the dying volcano. We rejoin him about noon on Monday:

> After that great thump, things gradually, but very slowly, moderated. Time seemed non-existent. However, by about four o'clock the wind dropped, but we only had a dim twilight till

6 p.m. when the weather cleared, but, as always in the tropics, darkness came on after 6. We had had no food or drink since breakfast and we went to the fo'c'sle for a feed. "Hard biscuit and a boiler of tea." Our throats were so choked with dust that we were glad of any kind of liquid. Very few remarks were made about what we had been through, but these were pretty lurid. Luckily we had plenty of bananas, a fruit almost unknown at home at that time. We sat round our boiler of tea—miserable-looking objects. There were Russian Finns, Germans, Negroes, English and Irish, four monkeys, a parrot and the dog, but no one was downhearted.

Not till the next morning did we get a glimpse of the coast, and what a sight! In place of luxuriant vegetation there was nothing but a brown sterile barrenness. The shores both of Java and Sumatra seemed to have been battered and burnt up. All sorts of wreckage was flying past us. And huge masses of vegetation floated by, on which we could see huge frogs, snakes and other strange reptiles: and the sharks! It was sickening to see them. We had been painting the ship and tarring the rigging, and we looked as if we had been through a shower of mustard.

The *Berbice*, hove to in the western approaches, was plunged in darkness until 8 p.m. Monday, but towards midnight the sky cleared slightly. It was still very dark next morning. Looking over the ship's side, the crew saw the vessel was hemmed in by floating pumice, and the decks were covered in ash. Forty tons were thrown overboard. The *Berbice* stayed where she was for five days and then sailed slowly through the Straits, encountering, says Captain Logan, the bodies of men and animals, including tigers from the jungles.

Feeble daylight reappeared at Batavia on Tuesday morning, though it remained dark for two more days. During Monday afternoon telegraph messages were received from towns in Bantam, situated behind the coast. They confirmed that terrible disaster had struck the Straits. By 10 p.m., twelve hours after Krakatoa's final explosion, it was known in Batavia that many towns and villages had been destroyed. Editors of news agencies cabled the information to the world's capitals.

10. Sound and Fury

A NEWS FLASH from Batavia, dated August 27, alerted the world to the volcanic disaster in the Sunda Straits. It had one curious result. The Boston *Globe* received a short version of the story which read:

> A terrific volcanic eruption took place last night on the island of Krakatoa. The detonations were heard and the flashes were visible here. Stones fell at Serang and ashes at Cheribon. Serang was in total darkness and this city nearly so. Communication with Anjer completely cut off.

News Editor Byron Soames sensed the magnitude of the story. The other city newspapers, he knew, would receive far more detailed reports from the Associated Press, from whose cables the *Globe* was barred. Soames went to the public library where he soaked himself in the geography and volcanic history of Java and Sumatra. Returning to his office, he wrote what proved to be an amazingly accurate picture of the disaster. Incorrectly, he stated that sixteen major volcanoes were in eruption, a news item which he may have received by cable, for this wild statement was published in many parts of the world. Soames's three articles, published on successive days, were much admired and many newspapers copied them, some reporting that twenty volcanoes were in eruption and that all the principal cities and towns of both Java and Sumatra had been destroyed.

The veracity of Soames's story was questioned only by the *Scotsman* which, in its issue of September 4th, remarked, "Someone in New York has dreamed a dream of earthquake

142

and tidal wave and carried his dream to market." Whether
or not this criticism gave it impetus, the story grew up many
years later that Soames, now renamed Edward Samson,
dreamed the eruption of Krakatoa while it happened, during
the evening August 27th, allowing for the difference in time.
The story is derived, more probably, from some jocular remark
made by Soames. When asked from where he derived his information, he may have said, "I dreamt it." The legend goes
like this:

In Boston, that Sunday evening was hot and sultry. In the
offices of the *Globe*, News Editor Edward Samson dozed in his
chair. He fell into fitful sleep, his subconscious mind plagued by
a terrible dream. He awoke at 3 a.m. shaken and dripping with
perspiration. He had seen a whole island in some distant ocean
blown apart. A huge volcano erupted; steaming lava flowed
down its sides, the sea rose in boiling steam, flaming debris
filled the sky, a mushroom cloud rose into the air. He saw natives caught between the floods of red-hot lava and the boiling
sea, rivers of mud engulfing them. Finally came a great explosion and the island disappeared from his view. Each detail was
clear and distinct. He jotted them down as he remembered.
As he wrote, he recalled the name of the island, Pralappe, in
the Sunda Strait between Sumatra and Java.

Samson initialled his note and headed it "Important." He put
it on the editor's desk and went home to bed. When the editor
found it, he thought it had come over the wire during the
night. He ran it next day under banner headlines. It caused a
sensation. Other newspapers took it up and it was carried from
coast to coast.

The editor was waiting for Samson when he came back on
duty. Asked for further details, he explained it was only a dream.
He was promptly dismissed and the editor set about the unhappy
task to admitting he had been hoaxed. Then reports of strange
phenomena began to pour in from many parts of the world:
shores were being lashed by giant tidal waves, shock waves were
encircling the earth, a gigantic dust cloud was sweeping across
the Indian Ocean. Could Samson's experience have been only
a dream, the editor wondered? It was easy to check. Opening

an atlas, he searched for an island in the East Indies named Pralappe. It didn't exist. But he was not satisfied; he investigated further. Pralappe, he learned, was the old native name for the island of Krakatoa. It hadn't been used for one hundred years.

The story is quite fictitious. Soames did not dream the story he wrote. Pralappe was not an old name for Krakatoa. The true facts have been disclosed by Jess Stearn in *Door of the Future.** So much for another oft-quoted example of the supernatural.

One statement in the story is true. Hours before news of Krakatoa's outburst reached the outside world, millions of people were experiencing its aftereffects. Outward from Krakatoa moved a sound wave, a sea wave, a pressure wave, a cloud of volcanic dust, and a sea of floating pumice.

Krakatoa's Big Bang ranged over one-thirteenth of the surface of the earth. It was heard by thousands of people, most of them thinking the noises came from a vessel in distress or from distant cannonading. In one place, at least, the unusual roars and rumblings aroused guilty consciences.

At Karimon Island, Java (355 miles), natives put to sea in their proas, believing a vessel to be in distress. At Toelong Agong (400 miles), English trader Edward St. George was mystified by the noises which he thought were like "great guns being fired at regular intervals." It must be Dutch soldiers, he concluded. Further away, at Surabaya, the English crew of the *Sea Witch*, which had been driven ashore, disbelieved a Dutch official who told them that the distant rumblings came from Krakatoa, 507 miles distant. Krakatoa's crash of doom was heard clearly throughout the island of Sumatra. A fearful noise was noted at 11 a.m. at Padang, 512 miles from the volcano. At Acheon (1,073 miles) the bangs so alarmed the Dutch, who were at war with the natives, that troops were placed under arms in the belief that an outlying fort was under attack. The master of the British ship *Devonhurst*, approaching Acheon, was awakened by a shock which led him

---

* Doubleday, New York, 1963.

to think the steamer had stranded. He rushed on deck and found his vessel in deep water on her proper course.

Mysterious sounds were heard throughout Malaya. At Singapore (522 miles), the master attendant of the Port despatched two ships to search for a vessel that was assumed to be firing guns in distress. On Monday the mile-long telephone line from Singapore to the island of Ishore was put out of action for several hours, an official stating afterwards, "On raising the tubes a perfect roar, as if of a waterfall, was heard, and by shouting at the top of one's voice, the clerk at the other end heard the voice, but not a single sentence was understood. The same noise, but to a lesser extent, was noticed on every line here, and sometimes, while listening to the Ishore line instruments, a report like a pistol shot was heard." At Penang, the explosion heard at 11 a.m. was mistaken for a salute fired by an American corvette that had sailed at 7 a.m.

The Hon. F. C. P. Vereker, commanding the British naval frigate *Magpie,* lying at anchor at Banquey Island, Borneo, 1,235 miles from the scene of the disaster, heard the bang distinctly, recording it in his log. A German resident at St. Lucia Bay, L. von Donop, reported, clearly with after knowledge of the event, "The noise of the eruption was heard all over Borneo. The natives inland, who murdered poor Witti, when they heard the noise, thought we were coming to attack them, and bolted from their village."

The "inexplicable detonation" was heard at Saigon and Bangkok in southeast Asia, at distances of 1,164 and 1,413 miles respectively, at Manila in the Philippines (1,800 miles), throughout the Celebes, and at Timor (1,351 miles). Government steamers at both islands put to sea to investigate, their crews returning bewildered. At Salwatty Island, New Guinea (1,800 miles), the Rajah asked Dr. F. H. Guillemand why the whites were firing cannon. The sound waves crossed the Indian Ocean to the Andaman Islands (1,500 miles), and they were heard distinctly in Ceylon, over 2,000 miles distant from Krakatoa. Steamers and canoes were despatched to trace their origin.

People living in certain towns in Ceylon noticed a whole

sequence of reports, in rapid succession, ending in a loud burst. An official at Badulla concluded that some volcano must be in eruption, but he could not imagine where it might be, thinking that a new one must have arisen in the sea. Others attributed the sounds to quarry blasting or a vessel in distress. Several observers stated they heard strange sounds during the night of August 26–27. At the island of Diego Garcia (2,267 miles) the captain of a French ship consulted with his lieutenant whether they should put to sea to aid some vessel in distress.

By far the most remarkable record comes from the island of Rodriguez, 2,968 miles across the Indian Ocean. On August 27th, for four hours preceding 3 p.m. the chief of police, James Wallis, heard distant roars which he attributed to a vessel firing out to sea. Krakatoa's explosions were also heard by numerous vessels navigating the Indian Ocean.

People living in Western Australia, between 1,200 and 1,900 miles from the scene of the eruption, were startled by loud reports. An observer at Victoria Plains heard noises from 11 p.m. on Sunday until 4 p.m. Monday. The bangs perplexed Commander Coghlan, Royal Navy, at Perth; they sounded like distant gunfire, although he knew that no warship was at exericise. At Alice Springs, one man attributed the sounds to rock-blasting; another thought someone was firing a rifle.

The prevailing trade wind carried Krakatoa's blasts further to the west than to the east. Travelling at the speed of sound, between 757 and 781 miles per hour, depending upon the temperature of the atmosphere, the noise, audible to the human ear, took four hours to reach its furthest recorded extent, at Rodriguez. Never before or since has a sound been heard at such great distances. By comparison, the noise made by the detonation of a thermonuclear weapon is trivial. Theoretically the maximum distance that a 1-megaton explosion can be heard is one hundred miles. How far such explosions *have been* heard is not stated in nuclear literature.

The inaudible and far more powerful pressure wave circled the earth no less than seven and one-half times, and its transits

were discernible on barographs six days later. Calculations of
the speed attained by the wave established that the blast left
its birth point about 10 a.m., Sunday, August 27th, a time
which is corroborated by the oscillations of the gas gauge at
Batavia, where the wave was recorded at 10.11 a.m., eight
minutes after it left Krakatoa. The wave rushed round the
world at or near the speed of sound, there being a difference
of twenty-eight miles per hour between its journey with and
against the earth's rotation. The times at which the wave
passed and repassed certain places was worked out in 1888 by
Lt. General R. Strachey, F.R.S., chairman of the Meteorological
Council. He computed its passages at Greenwich mean time,
seven hours from Indonesian time.

The outward wave passed over Sydney, Australia, at 8.24,
43.18 and 78.39 hours, and on its return journeys at 33.55 and
69.25 hours. Four hours and eighty-seven minutes elapsed between its origin and its first passage; 34 hours 90 minutes, and
35 hours 35 minutes, between its first and third; and its third
and fifth passages. Three passages were recorded on barographs at Tokyo, Japan; the intervals between the wave's
origin and first passage being noted as 5 hours 32 minutes.
By the time it first reached Rome, Italy, 9 hours 47 minutes
had elapsed, and the intervals between passages were recorded
as 35 hours 92 minutes. Paris, France, experienced the wave's
first passage 10 hours 15 minutes from its birth. Seven passages
were recorded at the Royal Observatory, Greenwich, England.
The wave arrived 10 hours 47 minutes after it left Krakatoa,
and it averaged between 36 hours 38 minutes on its westward
journey, and 35 hours 54 minutes on its eastward course. It
took 14 hours 35 minutes to reach New York, reappearing twice
at intervals of 37 hours 47 minutes.

It is difficult to learn at this distance of time which came
first, the oscillations of barographs or news of the volcanic disaster; or whether the two phenomena were immediately connected. Krakatoa's great explosion occurred at 10.02 a.m.,
Indonesian time. It was then 3.02 a.m. in London, the same
day. The wave took 17 hours 15 minutes to travel the distance,

passing over Greenwich Observatory at 10.15 that night, we
may conclude. London newspapers must have received cables
from Java about this time, for brief news of the eruption was
published next morning. Nonetheless, the sudden increase of
pressure must have puzzled scientists for some hours, just as
they were perplexed again at 9.30 p.m. on June 29, 1908, when
the barographs "fairly sizzled." The origin of the pressure
wave of August 27, 1883, was quickly established; twenty-two
years elapsed before Soviet scientists learned that a crashing
meteorite in distant Siberia had caused the disturbance in
1908.

Two Soviet science fiction writers (New York *Times*, March
20, 1964) now argue that the Siberian "meteorite" was in
reality a response from the inhabitants of a planet in the con-
stellation Cygnus to the "light signal" observed in 1883 when
Krakatoa exploded, a theory based on the belief, for which
there is no evidence, that the great explosion was accompanied
by an intense flash of flame.

The behaviour of the pressure wave in 1883 was examined
by the Krakatoa committee of the Royal Society of London,
which reported "the observed facts clearly establish that the
successive repetitions of the disturbance at numerous stations,
after varying intervals of time, were caused by the passage
over them of an atmospheric wave or oscillations, propagated
over the surface of the globe from Krakatoa as a centre, and
then expanding in a circular form, till it became a great circle
at a distance of 180 degrees from its origin; after which it advanced, gradually contracting again, to a node at the antipodes
of Krakatoa; when it was reflected or reproduced, travelling
backwards again to Krakatoa, from whence it once more returned in its original direction; and in this manner its repetition was observed not fewer than seven times at many of the
stations, four passages having been those of the wave travelling
from Krakatoa, and three those of the wave travelling from its
antipodes, subsequent to which its traces were lost."

The wave, observes the report, gradually became deformed
during its progress from and to the point where it originated,

and eventually lost its characteristics. The irregularity of the form of the wave, and its want of persistency, together with the considerable time over which it extended, led to some unavoidable uncertainty in fixing the exact moments of its passage over various stations. But, the report emphasises, the deep depression that immediately followed the initial rise appeared as the most persistent and easily recognisable feature in the first two passages of the wave.

Even more remarkable, perhaps, were the distances reached by the seismic, often inaccurately termed "tidal," sea wave, the wall of water which submerged the coasts of Java and Sumatra between 10.30 a.m. and 12.30 p.m. on August 27th. The genesis of the wave requires later discussion as it is bound up with the events at Krakatoa. It is necessary to recall that the great wave was preceded and followed by smaller waves which swept the shores of the Sunda Strait on Sunday evening, and that the fluctuations of the sea did not die away until Monday night. These waves were both "long" and "short"; technicalities with which we do not need to concern ourselves yet. The abnormal waves set up by Krakatoa's eruption spread more freely to the west, into the deep Indian Ocean, then to the east, where they were restricted by the narrowness of the channel, by the shallowness of the Java Sea, and by the archipelago by which it is surrounded.

The eastward waves dissipated quickly, causing no disturbance on tide gauges at Surabaya (440 miles) and Singapore (522 miles). Nevertheless, some rise in sea levels was experienced on the American Pacific seaboard, though whether these were caused by Krakatoa's waves is doubtful.

The wave which left Krakatoa shortly after ten o'clock fanned out across the Indian Ocean in a long undulation that does not appear to have been noticed by vessels at sea. It arrived at Port Blair, in the Andaman Islands, 1,480 miles to the north, on August 27th at 1355 hours. This was the first of a series of waves which continued until evening, at intervals of 2 hours 06 minutes, and which travelled at 308 miles per hour.

On the coasts of Ceylon (1,760 miles) the sea receded before the waves rushed up, as the Ceylon *Observer* reports:

> *Galle, 27th August*—An extraordinary occurrence was witnessed at the wharf at about 1.30 p.m. to-day. The sea receded as far as the landing stage on the jetty. The boats and canoes moored along the shore were left high and dry for about three minutes. A great number of prawns and fishes were taken up by the coolies and stragglers about the place, before the water returned. A similar phenomenon took place on the 31st December 1881, at about 8 a.m., shortly after the shock of an earthquake was experienced. Since the above was written, the sea has receded twice throughout the harbour.

Another Galle correspondent writes:

> A remarkable phenomenon occurred this afternoon at 3.30 p.m. in Galle harbour, the water of the sea receding from the shore to a considerable distance and returning in a short time to its usual limits. This occurred three or four times. As such phenomena are known to be connected with earthquakes it would be interesting to enquire if any shock was felt anywhere in the island.

At Colombo at 2.30 p.m., the sea rose fifteen inches above the highest level ever recorded, the tide ebbing forty-five minutes later, leaving the jetties high and dry and causing consternation amongst boatmen. It returned fifteen minutes later, rising high above normal, and this was followed by four more rises and falls. The disturbance continued all day and was still observable next morning. Its cause was attributed by one observer to the "subsistence of some submarine volcano."

The wave flooded a belt of land at Negombo, further to the north; and at Mannâr, a building situated 255 feet from the shore was damaged. The wave came and went thirteen times at Trincomalee on Ceylon's east coast, the rise and fall there averaging four feet.

Krakatoa's wave took another life at Arugain Bay, on the southeast coast of Ceylon. Three women, a child and a man were crossing the harbour bar. A big wave washed them inland, the water reaching to the man's chest. They were tumbled about in the water, being rescued by fishermen, one woman dying of her injuries. In his report, the harbour master stated, "I was further informed by the masters of ships anchored in the Bay that they felt all of a sudden their vessels go downward until they plainly saw the ground, and the ships were drawn seawards, and the people on the shore declared the anchors were exposed to sight. After this, the wave came in and raised the vessels and overflowed the bar."

The Government agent at Hambantota, Ceylon's most southerly station, reported that, on the afternoon of August 27th "between the hours of 12 and 2 o'clock, the sea kept on rising several feet above its ordinary level, and receding to a great distance, leaving the jetty almost dry, the water at the extreme end of it not being more than knee-deep. About every 20 minutes the sea completely covered the jetty, and rose so high that it washed away one of the old surf-boats that was high and dry near the main road. I sent out a canoe to bring back the boat, but the current was so strong that it was impossible to save it, and it was carried with great rapidity across the Bay and then dashed to pieces on the opposite shore. The waves did not, as is sometimes the case, break on shore with violence, but the sea rose gradually and similarly receded, and I must say, judging from examinations of the shore, that it must have risen 12 feet or more, above its ordinary level. The fishermen, with some difficulty, saved the canoe, and with the help of a large gang of prisoners, the cargo boat was saved from being carried out to sea. The oldest inhabitants never previously witnessed such an occurrence, and they considered it worthy of notice."

Waves lashed the coasts of India. At Madras, 1,863 miles from Krakatoa, the disturbance began abruptly at 2.33 p.m. on August 27th, by the arrival of the first of a series of ten waves which came at irregular periods, and which were calculated to have travelled at a speed of 338 miles per hour. These waves, which were recorded at many places in the Bay of Bengal, do not appear to have exceeded fourteen inches in height. They reached places on the coast close to Calcutta, where a number of river boats were damaged. At Bombay, on India's west coast (2,483 miles) a wave of six inches was registered. The great wave reached Karachi at 6.40 p.m., the first of a series of sixteen, some of which were twelve inches in height. It carried on to Aden (3,642 miles) where seventeen waves were noticed between 5.50 p.m. and 11.45 that night.

The waves enjoyed free passage westwards across the Indian Ocean. Small oscillations were observed round the coasts of Mauritius. At Cassis, during the whole day, the water was coming and going, but the movement was not taken much notice of till about 1.30 p.m. The tide on that day did not rise as usual. The water came with a swirl round the point of the seawall, and in about a couple of minutes returned with the same speed. This took place several times. Similar phenomena occurred on the 28th, but to a much smaller extent.

At Port Louis a swirl of muddy water came round the harbour wall at thirteen hours thirty minutes, rising three feet above normal level in the Trou Fanfaron, a narrow channel, snapping the ten-inch hauser of the *Touareg*. Suddenly the water receded, leaving boats high and dry. Fifteen minutes later it came roaring back. The oscillations continued all day, not in high waves or billows, but in strong undulations. At Arsenal Bay, five miles from Port Louis, a coaster of 17-tons burden was cast on the bar. Five minutes later the sea hurled the vessel into Turtle Bay where, having made two or three rapid evolutions, it was thrown on shore.

Similar phenomena were observed at the Seychelles Islands (2,873 miles) and in the St. Brandon Islands where the sea came into the harbour of Cargados Garajos, according to Captain Rault of the *Evelina,* as "not a wave, not a billow, nor a high sea; the water was smooth, except where there were heads of coral, and there a few wavelets only were produced."

The wave travelled the 2,662 miles to St. Brandon at a speed of 370 miles per hour, it has been calculated.

At Rodriguez Island, about 1.30 p.m. on the 27th, the sea was all disturbed, resembling water boiling heavily in a pot, swinging the boats which were floating about in all directions. It was then low tide, and most of the boats were aground. This disturbance in the water made its appearance quite suddenly, lasted for about half an hour, and ceased as suddenly as it had commenced. At 2.30 p.m. a similar disturbance commenced again in the inner harbour, and the tide suddenly rose to a height of five feet eleven inches, with a current of about ten knots an hour to the westward, floating all the boats which were aground, and tearing them from their moorings. All this happened in a very few minutes, and then the tide turned with equal force to the eastward, leaving the boats which were close inshore suddenly dry on the beach, and dragging a large decked pinnace from heavy moorings and leaving her dry on the reef. At noon on the 29th the tide was about its usual height and appeared to be settled. The water was very muddy, and not nearly so salt as sea water usually is; it was little more than brackish.

Tidal disturbances were also observed on the west coast of Reunion Island, and especially at St. Pierre, on the southwest coast. The maximum height of this tide was about four feet. The flow took scarcely five minutes to rise, after which the water remained about a minute at rest, and then receded with the same rapidity, to rise again a minute after.

The tide gauge at Port Alfred, South Africa, 4,550 miles across the Indian Ocean, started to react at 7 a.m. on August 27th, registering at 5.10 p.m., a wave of 1 foot 4 inches in height. The maximum of 1 foot 6 inches was recorded at 11 p.m. A large wave, 4 feet in height, reached Port Elizabeth at 5.54 p.m., where it was followed by twenty-two more waves at intervals of 2 hours 24 minutes.

Great waves, ushered in by smaller undulations, were remarked at Cape Town for several hours on August 27th. The strongest wave reached eighteen inches in height, and the disturbances continued all day. Waves reaching fifteen inches in height were also noticed at Port Moltke, South Georgia, by the tide gauge of the German South Polar Expedition, and at Cape Horn, 7,520 miles east and 7,820 miles west of Krakatoa.

The earliest wave is believed to have followed the longer passage, where it was unfettered by islands, achieving the speed of 347 miles per hour. Whether Krakatoa's wave crossed 11,470 miles of sea to reach Colon, on the Isthmus of Panama, where sixteen waves were noticed, is thought doubtful, as the disturbances may have been of local character.

Tidal disturbances were noted at ports on the Bay of Biscay and in the English Channel on August 28th. At Cherbourg (10,780 miles) five waves arrived at intervals of thirty-six minutes between 9.20 and 11.44 a.m. Their average range was two inches. Undulations of one inch were recorded at Havre. There were slight rises at Portland and Devonport, where a six-inch wave was registered at 10.43 a.m. It was followed by four others, at intervals of sixty-five minutes. The speed of the wave from Krakatoa was calculated at 380 miles per hour.

Waves were also remarked in Australia and New Zealand, and they continued across the Pacific, being noticed at Honolulu, Kodiak in Alaska and, perhaps, at San Francisco, where the sea rose at intervals between August 27th and 30th. If these undulations were caused by Krakatoa's wave, it travelled the 10,340 miles at the prodigious speed of 594 miles per hour.

A wide and thick layer of pumice floated from the Straits into the Indian Ocean. Ships ploughed through it for months; three months after the eruption a passenger on one ship, Stanley M. Rendall, who described his experience in a letter published in *Nature*, noticed that an iron bar thrown over the ship's side rested on the surface of the mass instead of sinking, and he saw trunks of trees and corpses embedded in the pumice. In his letter he noted, "The passage of our vessel left a wake of only a few feet, which speedily closed in again, so that to see it at all I had to lean over the stern and look under as it were. It seemed exactly as if we were steaming through dry land, the ship acting as a plough, turning up on each side of her a large mound of pumice, especially noticeable on looking over the bows. Our passage through this made no great noise—just a soft sort of crushing sound. The effect was very striking and queer."

The *W. H. Besse* encountered wide sheets of pumice, on which lay the bodies of men and fish intermingled with green cocoanuts, six hundred miles west of Java Head; and Captain Baker noticed that for a thousand miles the sea was dull grey.

The Royal Society of London received many such reports from sixty-four ships which crossed the Indian Ocean between August 27, 1883, and November 11, 1884. All encountered pumice, and another correspondent noted a thick layer off the coast of Natal, South Africa, on September 27–28, 1884.

Krakatoa's dust cloud, propelled by the southeast wind, spread out across the Indian Ocean. Within a few days it formed an arc of twilight, 300,000 square miles in extent, and it dropped part of its mass over 1,100,000 square miles of ocean. The cloud rolled on, encircling the earth, and causing strange optical phenomena.

Verbeek calculated that the cloud of ash and pumice rose, on August 27th, thirty-one miles above Krakatoa, and it comprised 4.3 cubic miles of material. This figure must not be confused with the amount of Krakatoa's mass which was engulfed, a question which will be dealt with in Chapter 12. According to Verbeek, of this ejecta 2.86 cubic miles fell within ten miles of the volcano. The remainder spread into the atmosphere, where it reached an altitude of 100,000 feet, and floated away at the speed of seventy-three miles per hour.

Modern geologists and climatologists think that Verbeek's calculations of the mass of the ejecta was far too low. In the estimate of Mr. H. Wexler, of the United States Weather Bureau,* Krakatoa ejected thirteen cubic miles of lava, dust and mud, one-third of which fell in the Straits, another third fell within twenty miles, while the remainder, about four cubic miles, settled slowly from the atmosphere for several years.

Within one month, this mass of fine dust encircled the globe at the Tropics, spreading over half the world's surface. Yet it took two more months to reach the Northern Hemisphere and cover the additional 50 percent of the earth's surface. There is

---

* *Bulletin,* American Meteorological Society, Feb. 2, 1952.

strong evidence, points out Wexler, that the edge of the cloud mass moved from west to east across Western Europe, beginning on November 23rd. Its journey round the earth gave rise to glorious sunrises and sets, and brilliant twilight glows. The Royal Society of London collected and published many eyewitness observations.

These strange manifestations of Krakatoa's might were first observed in a belt along the Tropics. An observer in India remarked on August 27th: "The sun had a greenish-blue tinge, and was somewhat dimmed by a haze in the afternoon. At 4 p.m. the colour was bluish. This gradually passed into a greenish colour, and this in turn became tinged with yellow as the sun approached the horizon. As the sun sank, bands of smoky haze drifted across its disc. After it was down, bright yellow, orange and red appeared in the west, a very deep red remaining for more than an hour after sunset; whereas under ordinary conditions all traces of colour leave the sky in this latitude within half an hour after the sun disappears. At night the moon, just past the first quarter, was surrounded by a pale greenish halo."

Reports of green, blue, and copper suns, and the obscuration of the atmosphere by silvery haze, came from Ceylon, South Africa, South America, and Australasia. The sunset at Yokohama, Japan, on August 29th, was described as "blood red." Green suns were observed at Panama on September 2nd and 3rd. At Hawaii, the sunset on October 2nd was "fiery red" and it spread a lurid glare over the heavens, producing a weird effect. When a "green sun" was observed in Madras on September 8th "some of the learned old-men" proclaimed it a "bad sign" and they foretold famine; a doleful prophesy which was not fulfilled. At Cape Town, on September 3rd, the western sky at sunset was described as "if lit by a conflagration." Seaman Dalby on the *Hope* in the middle of the Indian Ocean on September 18th, remarked "fine twilight glows."

By September 22nd, the dust cloud was widening and deepening. The observed optical effects show that it reached Mexico and northern Africa in the north, and Chile and Australia in the south, between that date and October 10th. It spread across the eastern United States, reaching Poughkeepsie, New York, and New Haven, Connecticut, where in both towns the lurid evening sky caused firemen to rush out seeking a non-existent blaze. Magnificent sun rises and sun sets were observed in Lisbon on October 15th, San Diego, California, on the 19th, Nashville, Tennessee, on the 29th, and Rome, Italy, on November 30th. The cloud reached Britain on November 23rd, as is proved by hundreds of "sightings." W. Ashcroft, living at Chelsea, London, painted six water colours of the "twilight and after glow effects" as he watched the sun set across the Thames. They are published in the Royal Society's report.

As the dust cloud spread out to cover an area of 135,000,000 square miles, argument developed. The generally accepted theory that the spectacular sky glows were the result of Krakatoa's dust cloud dimming the atmosphere was challenged by several scientists, who claimed their cause was (1) local everywhere, probably the result of an abundance of moisture in the atmosphere, (2) the tail of a comet through which the earth passed, (3) a cyclone in the sun's atmosphere.

The "volcanic dust" believers countered these arguments by sound logic. The phenomena were too widespread to be local in origin. The comet had broken up on September 9, 1882. The optical effects followed Krakatoa's eruption progressively and they could be traced back to that point. Samples of dust taken at widespread places matched Krakatoa's ejecta. Similar optical phenomena had been observed after many famous volcanic eruptions.

Remarkable sun glows had been experienced in Scandinavia in 1636, following the eruption of Mount Heckla in Iceland in the month of May. In 1680, the year in which Krakatoa first erupted, according to the Danish historian Birkerod, the heavens had been filled with blood-red light, and people had been terribly alarmed. Blood-red suns, at rise and set, were observed in many parts of Europe for four months in 1783, the year in which Mount Asama, Japan, and the Laki fissure at

Mount Shaplar in Iceland exploded. During the summer of
that year, says Gilbert White, the English naturalist, "a peculiar
haze or smoky fog prevailed for many weeks in this island and
in every part of Europe, and even beyond its limits. The heat
was so intense that butcher's meat could hardly be eaten the
day after it was killed, and flies swarmed so in the lanes and
hedges that they rendered the horses half frantic and made
riding irksome." Pink, red and green suns were observed all
over the world during the summer of 1815, the year of Tambora's great eruption on April 7th. Unusual optical effects were
remarked in England on June 28–29, eighty-two days later; a
remarkable coincidence when it is recalled that eighty-eight
days elapsed in 1883 between Krakatoa's eruption and the appearance of sun glows in England. As well as these similarities,
points out E. Douglas Archibald, in his report to the Royal
Society in 1888, there is a general coincidence between observed sky phenomena and volcanic eruptions over the last
three hundred years. Red twilights have followed every major
eruption, he remarks.

The argument that the remarkable sun-glows and other
optical phenomena were caused by Krakatoa's dust cloud
seems unassailable; but why did the cloud take approximately
three months to reach the Northern Hemisphere, after it had
encircled the globe at the Tropics within one month? Mr. E.
Wexler explains this anomaly in his article, *The Spread of
the Krakatoa Volcanic Dust Cloud As Related to High-Level
Circulation.* The absence of upper-air charts for 1883 neces-
sitated his use of normal 19 K.M. charts for the Northern
Hemisphere, which Mr. Wexler took as a guide to explain the
travel of the main portion of the cloud.

During the month of September, he says, the cloud was
mainly confined to the broad zonal easterly winds which are
characteristic of equatorial latitudes at that season. Rapid
lateral spread towards the Poles occurred, as eddies carried
portions of the cloud to higher latitudes. As the Northern
Hemisphere winter advanced, and the equatorial easterlies
diminished in extent, the dust cloud came more and more

under the influence of subtropical cellular circulations, and they accounted for the virtual cessation of the movement of the cloud westwards and its very slow advance northward. In November, as the air current system became displaced farther south, the dust was enabled to spread rapidly from west to east, and from south to north. If Krakatoa's explosion had occurred in winter or spring, the spread of the cloud into the Northern Hemisphere would have been far more rapid. As it was, the spread of the cloud in the Southern Hemisphere was much faster than in the Northern.

Of the many scientific controversies aroused by Krakatoa's outburst, few are more interesting, especially to the layman, than the question, "Did the eruption affect the world's weather?"

The theory that the absorption of the sun's rays by volcanic dust clouds reduces the earth's temperatures, and could even bring on an Ice age, is an ancient one. Benjamin Franklin advanced it in 1784, the year following the great eruptions in Iceland and Japan. The winter of 1783–84 was unusually severe, observed the Philadelphian naturalist. The abnormal weather which followed other major eruptions seems to support Franklin's theory.

Eighteen hundred and sixteen was known as the "year without a summer." In 1815 Tambora in Java erupted, its dust cloud drifting around the earth. The year 79, following the eruption of Vesuvius on August 24, was very cold in Europe, and long hard winters followed the eruptions of Vesuvius, 1631, Heckla, 1636 and 1694, Pelée in Martinique in 1902, and Katmai in Alaska in 1912.

Solar radiation readings taken at Lausanne, Switzerland, in November, 1902, dropped precipitately from 104 percent to 85 percent, and they did not return to 100 percent until May, 1904. At Warsaw, Poland, between January, 1901, and September, 1902, they were greater than average, dropping gradually and consistently to a minimum of 84 percent in February, 1903, and they did not return to normal until March, 1904. Mount Pelée in Martinique, erupted on May 9, 1902. Following the eruption of Mount Katmai on June 6, 1912, three solar-radiation stations, at Madison, Wisconsin, Mount Weather, Virginia, and Kew, London, recorded a decline until September, 1913. At Kew the fall was from 107 percent in June to 76 percent in July, and the readings did not return to normal until May, 1913. Decreases in solor radiation of 20 percent were registered in Algeria in June, 1912.

There is some evidence that abnormal weather conditions were experienced after the eruptions of Cotopaxi, in Ecuador, 1855–1856, Merapi in Java in 1872, Tarawera, New Zealand, 1886, in which year solar radiation percentages dropped to 75; Bogoslov, in the Aleutians, 1890, Quizapii, Chile, 1932, and Mount Spur, Alaska, and Hibokhibok in the Philippines in 1953.

Meteorologists do not accept that the evidence that volcanic eruptions affect the weather to any considerable extent is conclusive. The winter which Benjamin Franklin remarked as being abnormally severe was preceded in Europe by an unusually hot summer. During the summer of 1912, following the eruption of Katmai on June 6th and 7th, the transparency of the atmosphere in the United States was much affected by dust, and the effect reached its maximum in June when, at Mount Wilson Observatory, direct radiation from the sun was reduced by nearly 20 percent.

The eruptions of a volcano in Bali, Indonesia, between February and May, 1963, "upset the whole rain balance throughout the world," according to Dr. Aden Meinel of the Stuart Observatory, Tucson, Arizona.* Dr. Meinel's theory is based on the belief that the Balinese eruptions threw up into the atmosphere twin layers of dust which encircled the earth at altitudes of 73,000 and 150,000 feet. This dust had produced very heavy rainfall throughout the Southern Hemisphere, he says. The deserts of Chile and other normally dry South American coastal lands were deluged with up to twenty inches of rain in the months following the eruptions. On the other hand, normally moist areas of the Northern Hemisphere had so little

Interview, New York *Journal-American*, Oct. 26, 1963.

rain that drought conditions existed. It is a case, he says, of the Southern Hemisphere receiving an over-abundance of rain, while the Northern Hemisphere has been short-changed. This dust, Dr. Meinel suggests, is moving northwards and as it accumulates, "it is entirely possible that we will receive heavy rains and heavy snows." (It may be remarked that the winter of 1963–64 was abnormally dry in Western Europe, and the summer cold and wet in New Zealand.)

Enough dust, observes Dr. Meinel, has drifted into the Northern Hemisphere to produce a series of spectacular sunrises and sets, the length and breadth of the United States. "We are being treated to a rare event in the history of the world," Dr. Meinel told his interviewer.

The possible effect on the world's weather of the dust cloud ejected into the atmosphere by Krakatoa in 1883 has been discussed by several climatologists.

Mr. H. Wexler examined "The Effect of Krakatoa's Dust Cloud on the Weather in the *Bulletin* of the American Meteorological Society.* Only one solar-radiation station, at Montpellier, France, existed in 1883, he points out. The observations taken there were made by a pyrheliometer pointing at the sun at noon whenever it was visible.

Beginning in December, 1882, the mean values stayed at 100 percent or higher, except in June, 1883. In November the peak value of 115 percent of normal was reached. In December it dropped to 90 percent and in January, 1884, to 82 percent. It did not return to a value higher than 103 percent during the next three years, and it reached a minimum value of 76 percent in August and September, 1885. The average value for the period December, 1883, to October, 1886, was 91 percent; a low value, not again reached over a period of equal length. The marked drop in radiation values, Wexler remarks, from November to December, 1883, coincides with the beginning of the prominent optical effects observed in Western Europe. From October 3, the Montpellier daily radiation values stayed

---

* January 1, 1952.

consistently above 100 percent, reaching a peak of 130 percent on November 28th. It dropped to 80 percent on December 5th, and to 75 percent on the 8th, and rose to 111 percent on December 12th, the average observation being 88 percent.

It took, we know, approximately three months for the cloud to travel to Western Europe in concentrations large and persistent enough to produce the unusual and prolonged optical effects which were seen. Coincidental with the appearance of these phenomena, the solar-radiation values at Montpellier decreased by 25 percent and they remained below normal for three years. Thus, observes Mr. Wexler, "both optical and radiation observations therefore agree in placing the appearance of Krakatoa's cloud in Europe some three months after the explosions."

Volcanic dust may decrease direct radiation from the sun by as much as 20 percent, says Mr. Wexler, but that does not mean, he emphasises, that there will be 20 percent less *total* solar radiation reaching the ground, since the decrease in direct solar radiation will be compensated for by an increased amount of scattered radiation from the sky. The dust, he says, acting as a scattering medium, should return about half of the 20 percent depleted direct solar radiation to space and the other half to the earth, so that the decrease in total solar and sky radiation should be of the order of 10 percent.

Meteorologists agree that Krakatoa's dust cloud reduced direct solar radiation by some 10 percent. Did that result in any marked weather changes?

Professor J. Gentilli * does not rate the likelihood high. The average mean temperature in the years 1884–1886 dropped only one-quarter of a degree below normal average. Western and Central Europe experienced in 1884 above average temperatures, as did Northeastern Asia, Alaska, and sections of the eastern states of North America, and it was also warmer than usual in parts of the Southern Hemisphere, in eastern Australia and the Argentine. On the other hand, it was cooler

---

* *Geological Magazine* 85.72. 1948.

than usual in Russia, Siberia, India, China, Canada, most of the United States, and in Chile, parts of Australia, and South Africa. The area in which temperatures were below average was greater than that in which they were above average. Summing up, Professod Gentilli of the University of Australia says, "There appears to be no climatological evidence to support the theory that volcanic eruptions may cause a lowering of temperatures even in the year immediately following the eruption and even in regions very near to the erupting volcano."

W. J. H. Humphreys,* who Mr. Wexler describes as "the stoutest advocate of the theory of vulcanism in an attempt to explain climatic variations," suggests that the simultaneous eruption of volcanoes can affect the sun's radiation throughout the world for several years, and V. E. Fuchs ** is of the opinion that large-scale volcanic activity over long periods can cause marked lowering of world temperature and may lead to the onset of Ice ages.

It would require a very long period of sustained volcanic activity of catastrophic type, in which vast volumes of pumice were ejected, to bring on an Ice age, claims Mr. Wexler, who remarks that geologists have noticed that although some Ice ages were preceded by volcanic activity, as is shown by the study of ocean sediments, other Ice ages have occurred without any preceding or current volcanic activity. Many periods of intense volcanic activity occurred without any accompanying period of glaciation.

J. Murray Mitchell, Jr., also of the United States Weather Bureau, writing in the *Annals* of the New York Academy of Sciences,*** observes that an eruption in extra-tropical latitudes of one hemisphere does not spread dust into the other hemisphere in sufficient quantity to alter its heat budget materially, and he remarks that examination of data shows "a consistent tendency for (violent) eruptions to be followed by a lower

---

* *Journal* of the Franklin Institute 176, 131. 1913.
** *Geological Magazine* LXXXIV 321-27.
*** October 1961.

five-year average temperatures in the eruption hemisphere, and that they give some credence to the possibility that the very low global temperatures of the latter 1880's and early 1890's were primarily attributable to the eruption of Krakatoa in 1883." It is conceivably possible, also, he says, that the relatively rapid rate of cooling in the Northern Hemisphere within recent years has been due in significant part to the Mount Spur, Alaska, eruption in 1953 and the great Bezymyannaya, Kamchatka, eruption of 1956, the intensity of which the Russian scientist, G. S. Gorshkov, has ranked with those of Krakatoa and Pelée.

The observations of these meteorologists leave us with another interesting question. If Krakatoa's eruption had no marked effect on the world's weather, how does that conclusion affect the current controversy about nuclear weapons, the explosion of which, according to many people, caused bad (never good) weather?

D. J. Mason of the Imperial College, London, answers the question thus:[*] Atomic explosions, he says, might cause *local* disturbance, and he points out that a modest thunderstorm releases as much energy as 10 A-bombs, and the energy dissipated in a hurricane could not be matched by the explosion of several hundred H-bombs. An H-bomb, he says, has energy of the magnitude comparable with those of such natural calamities as the eruption of Krakatoa in 1883 and of the Siberian meteorite of 1908, though of considerably less intensity, and he draws this conclusion: "The dust-clouds produced by the volcanic eruption of 1883 . . . reduced incoming radiation by almost 10 percent . . . without, however, reducing corresponding noticeable changes in the average surface temperature and rainfall. The effect of the Hydrogen bomb, probably 1,000 times less powerful than Krakatoa, must be correspondingly smaller."

Commenting on this statement, Professor Willard H. Parsons, chairman of the Department of Geology, Wayne State Uni-

---

[*] *Weather*, May 1955.

versity, Detroit, Michigan, in a letter to the author dated April 14, 1964, remarks, "Krakatoa probably released one million times more energy than the largest H-bomb yet set off."

Mr. Samuel Glasstoni, the editor of *The Effects of Nuclear Weapons*, 1957, has also considered the problem: "The dust raised in severe volcanic explosions, such as that of Krakatoa in 1883, is known to cause a noticeable reduction in the sunlight reaching the earth, but it has not been established that this decrease has any great effect on the weather. The amount of debris remaining in the atmosphere after the explosion of even the largest nuclear weapon is probably not more than about 1 percent or so of that raised by the Krakatoa eruption. Further, solar radiation records reveal that none of the nuclear explosions to date have resulted in any detectable change in the direct sunlight recorded on the ground." The general opinion of meteorologists is, he says, that nuclear explosions have no known influence on the weather.

Krakatoa's sound and fury swept on round the world. The last echoes of the controversies aroused have not yet died away.

11. All Gone

THE BLACKOUT in the Straits persisted, more or less, for three days. Within an area of 130 miles it was dark for twenty-four hours, within fifty miles for fifty-seven hours. Heavy seas pounded the ravaged coastlines. Wild disorder and confusion reigned. The survivors of the disaster were homeless and destitute; there was no food, no water, no fodder for cattle. Ash and pumice clogged the ground, hung from every tree, and choked wells and rivers. Roads were destroyed, bridges broken, boats smashed. In the ruined villages and towns stalked fearful shapes, looting and stealing. "The Arch Fiend stood everywhere, implacable, unpitying, offering help to none, listening to no imploration," claimed one wretched survivor, his mind unhinged by his experience. Corpses of men and animals floated in the sea and lay on land, a prey to the wild beasts prowling from the jungles. To the havoc of flood and fire, fear of pestilence was added. Distracted people sought husbands and fathers, wives and children. Despairingly, they gazed at the waste of waters, as if to implore the sea to give back its dead.

The Dutch rose to the occasion with remarkable promptitude and despatch. Their fortunes were at stake; their rich plantations, their roads, quarries and ports were gone, their labourers decimated and demoralized. A Central Committee for the Relief of Sufferers from the Outburst of Krakatoa was appointed; money poured in from near and far. The Prince of Orange headed the relief fund in Holland. Messrs. Krupps of Essen sent 6,000 florins. Batavia plunged into an orgy of festivity to raise funds, the *Bode* commenting; "Countless are the schemes suggested for a more general laying of offerings on the altar of charity, and the surest way to succeed therein is certainly to turn the human desire for recreation to account by the exercise of benevolence. In other words, it is intended to set on foot festivities and all manner of amusements to ensure a more abundant flow of donations. Should it prove successful, the fact will show that society in Java steadily longs for recreative amusements, perhaps by way of a relief from business cares, but certainly owing to the sameness of the life led here day by day."

Ships were despatched to the stricken areas. The *Ophir* sailed for Merak, the *Kederie* to Telok Betong; a dredger only was sent to Anjer for there was nothing and no one to rescue there. Mr. Levyssohn Norman, a member of the Council of the Indies, was ordered to Bantam with Dr. Sollewyn Gelphe. Mr. Struick, a former chief secretary, hurried to the Lampongs.

The full extent of the disaster could only be imagined. Nothing was known of the Lampongs and southern Sumatra. The reports from Bantam were appalling. The number of casualties was estimated at forty, fifty, sixty thousand. The calamity was "more fearful than the most timid mind could suggest," stated the Algeeman *Dagblad*. "The gloomiest forbodings fell short of reality," it said. "All gone. Plenty lives lost" came a message from Serang, Bantam's capital.

The reports made by various visitors are our best guide to the state of the plain of Bantam, between hills and sea.

Dr. Sollewyn Gelphe reached Batavia on his return from the devastated area on September 7th. The newspaper published his report next day:

At the foot of these hills and between the extremities of their outlying spurs, a dense population dwelt in numerous villages, on an alluvial plain. The tract of country, for instance, on which Tjaringin, the chief town, stood, was many miles long. Like Anjer, the town of Tjaringin, besides a great many villages, no longer exists since the 27th August. As far as the eye can reach, the only thing that remains standing there is a solitary tree, a gigantic durian, maimed, branchless, and leafless. It forms the gravemark of a heap of corpses and carcasses lying under roofs, houses, and trunks of trees. Hundreds of such graves, though of smaller dimensions, may be seen over and over again on the plain. The turned-up earth often merely covers a corpse, alongside which a cocoanut branch or bamboo is stuck upright for the guidance of the authorities.

Thousands of corpses of human beings and also carcasses of animals still await burial, and make their presence apparent by an indescribable stench. They lie in knots and entangled masses impossible to unravel, and often jammed along with cocoanut stems among all that had served these thousands as dwellings, furniture, farming implements, and adornments for houses and compounds.

The roads in that neighbourhood are unrecognizable. In the European quarter the foundations of houses serve as waymarks. The assistant Resident's dwelling house with its six rooms is reduced to six compartments separated by brick walls and filled with decomposing sea water. At his office, the floor only is left, the remainder having disappeared. The houses of the Regent and Contrôleur also have disappeared from their foundations. The fields, strewn with corpses, offer an unusually animated scene in spite of their horrors. Contrôleur Tromp has taken vigorous action for burying the corpses at the rate of 5 guilders apiece. For this purpose, men are called up from each village separately. But along with the gravediggers, thousands of people come provided with handspikes or sharpened stakes, to be serviceable to them as implements either in searching for their own property or in robbing what belonged to others. For robbery is the only object for which hundreds of all ages and both sexes are disposed to venture going to Tjaringin, where but few police are available. On my approach a group of them dispersed, to return forthwith, like hyenas scared from a battle field, should the check on them be removed. Many gangs remained, robbing on as if they were owners of the articles which they dug up. Some of the robbers are aware of the whereabouts of the missing Government cash boxes. At least, this must be inferred from the considerable amounts of money found on several persons who were arrested near Pandeglang.

The affecting sight presented to spectators by the corpses and their gravediggers need not be described in a report like this, but it is worth mentioning that no corpse can be recognised, not even by its nationality, so that all the stories about recognition of corpses must not be believed. In that quarter, the limit of the havoc wrought by the tidal wave extends along the hill range between Tjaringin and Anjer 1 to 1½ miles from the sea, and 5 or 7 miles from it within the district of Penimbang. To villages on these hills, and even still higher ones, thousands fled, thinking that at any moment the wave might again come on, and hence were unwilling to return. But in fact, returning to these carrion fields with their pools and lagoons of rotting sea water is now impossible.

Meanwhile the fugitives remain a burden on the inhabitants. In one village, that of Taloon, containing 60 families, I found 500 persons from the coast plain, of whom only one half had food supplies. With praiseworthy zeal, the authorities are taking measures to remove this burden from the less suffering people. In this respect it is necessary to mention that the European refugees also, at least those from Tjaringin, met with help and assistance everywhere on their journey. In that time of anxiety and commotion, the villagers took the trouble to offer them coffee and other refreshments, and even to carry the weak and wounded among them. Such facts render unfair complaint doubly hateful. What the newspapers have related of the unfeeling conduct of the inhabitants of Tjalegon may be true, but the particulars of the accompanying circumstances have not been given in full. Thus I heard one of the rescued ladies complain of being unable to get a drink of water, but she did not tell what became apparent to me on inquiry, that the request for it was made in a village, the inhabitants of which were themselves, at that moment, fleeing hastily in deep darkness, amidst the strife of the elements.

Before I proceed with the description of the whole country, which, with the exception of the now devastated coast district, forms the seashore boundaries of the province of Bantam, the subject of the ash and mud showers must be dealt with. After a course of 22 miles in a straight line, the ashes cast out by Krakatoa on the West Coast of Java sunk to the stratum of air touching the firm ground. The quantities of ashes sank lower still, covering the ground and whatever stood thereon, but in the midst of this eruption a rain shower fell over a portion of the province of Bantam. The immediate consequence of it was that the ashy particles were carried along in the fall, and that the larger particles adhered together until no longer rain, but flakes of mud, fell, which sometimes were several square inches in size. Where the ashes fell without rain, or with only a little, they did slight harm, but where rain had clotted them into mud they destroyed leaves and branches by their weight. Moreover the mud was accompanied by a moist heat which scorched everything green around, while on drying it continued to stick to whatever it had struck on or against.

The Lloyd's agent at Batavia, a Scotsman named McColl, and Mr. Schuit, the agent at Anjer, made a tour of Bantam. Tjalegon they found was still completely covered with volcanic ash six weeks after the eruption, its plantations and gardens destroyed, its cocoanut trees weighed down by ash. Leaving their post carriage they got into kakars (native spring carts) which took them along the road to Merak. McColl tells the story:

> Proceeding a short distance, the effects of the volcanic wave were seen, the road having been carried away and great lagoons were formed inland. We soon had to leave our kakars and pro-ceed on foot, and after this it was a hot scramble of two hours along the beach over fallen trees and rocks before we arrived at what was formerly the important station of Merak. The entire distance traversed by us, about six miles, was one scene of desolation, which simply cannot be described or understood un-less seen. For miles there was not a tree standing, and where formerly stood numerous campongs (native villages), surrounded by paddy fields and cocoanut groves, there was nothing but a wilderness, more resembling the bottom of the sea than anything else, rocks of coral, stones, and sea shells strewn everywhere. Some of these solid masses of coral lying miles inward could not be less than 100 tons in weight.
> Arriving at Merak, the path was strewn with pieces of iron, while here and there were portions of the bedding and furniture of the houses of the Europeans, and everywhere shreds of native clothing, women's and men's badjus and sarongs. We were in-formed officially that the number of bodies buried in the district we came through was 2,700. Arriving at what was once the

centre of the Government quarry works for the Batavia harbour works, we climbed the small hill where the houses of the principal engineers and officials formerly stood. Of these there is literally not one stone left, and looking at the scene of desolation around, it was difficult to conceive that it had once been a busy place, employing over 1,000 people including families. Strewn about were massive iron trollies, engines, locomotives, fragments of iron columns, and rails torn up and twisted like wire. Of the large workshop erected on solid cement foundations supporting iron pillars nothing remained. Nothing also of the extensive stores, nor of the wharf at which the hopper barges were loaded.

The volcanic wave must, in my opinion, have been even higher than the general estimate of 100 feet, and I base my opinion on the fact that the official height of the small hill of Merak is 35 metres [115 feet] while the wave which swept away the houses must, of course, have been still higher than the top of the hill, and this additional height I estimate to be 20 feet. This fact I ascertained pretty accurately by a careful estimate of the height from the ground of wreckage attached to the stems of a couple of cocoanut trees still standing. This would give here, at all events, a total height of 135 feet.

On the top of this hill, the whole community of workmen took refuge when the first wave came at 6 a.m., and fancying themselves safe there, they returned again, when a second and much higher wave at 9 a.m.* came and swept them all away. On the foundation of one of the houses on the hilltop, Mr. Bursley, an American, formerly at Anjer, has erected a bamboo house, with flagstaff attached, and until something definite is settled about a new port of call, he has permission to make this a pilot station.

McColl and Schuit left Merak and made for Anjer, turning inland to avoid a long valley into which the sea had penetrated for six miles, forming a great lagoon. Not one stone of the old post station at Tjiadieng was left standing; building, men and horses having been swept away. Everywhere hundreds of people were at work repairing roads, clearing rubbish, burying corpses and strewing ash on the sea-swept soil in hope of future improvement. Reaching a hill on the outskirts of Anjer, they

---

* He means 10.30 a.m.

looked back towards Merak, eleven miles distant, and to the foothills four to five miles away. This wedge-shaped plain, forty square miles in extent, was one vast scene of desolation, having been completely swept by the waves. There was not a house nor a tree to be seen, where previously every plot of ground had been covered by houses and plantations.

Encircling the hill, McColl and Schuit came to the valley of Anjer, a semicircle of four miles from point to point, extending 2 miles inland, and flanked by a range of hills. There was nothing to be seen but lagoons and boulders strewn about, and not a vestige of Anjer itself.

We proceeded, however, and at length came upon the site of the town and fort. Of the fort there is almost nothing left, great blocks of masonry being cast inland; of the town still less, for not one stone is to be seen above another. Mr. Schuit, who lost seven of his relations, went to look for his house, but could not find a trace of it, and after a time he concluded that the river which formerly formed the creek had changed its course, and was flowing over the spot where his house and that of the assistant resident once stood.

It was difficult to realise that the town of Anjer had ever existed. Clothing and bedding was scattered about here and there, but otherwise there was, beyond the graves, nothing to show that a town and a score of kampongs had ever existed. I met here a most intelligent native official distributing rice to the people. He went with me to what was the European cemetery, on rising ground half a mile to the south of Anjer. There a number of people had taken refuge after the first wave at 6 p.m. on Monday, 27th. August, but were carried off by the second wave at 9 a.m. Many of the graves were completely scooped out, and what with the ash-rain and the effects of the volcanic wave there was not a trace of its ever having been a cemetery. Near here passed the conduit conveying the drinking water to Anjer, but it is entirely destroyed, and about a mile farther up the water is seen flowing into the fields.

At present the entire country outside the area covered by the volcanic wave is covered with ash, throwing off a strong glare; but in time it may be found to be the fertiliser of the soil.

Standing at the site of Anjer, McColl saw, looming in the distance, the old peak of Krakatoa. The rest of the island had disappeared as had now the low-lying banks of Steers and Calmeyer.

Concluding his story, McColl refuted some of the sensational news items that had been reported in the world newspapers. The statement that five thousand of the twenty-five thousand Chinese population of Batavia had perished was untrue. Not a life, Asiatic or European, had been lost in the capital. The report that eight hundred Europeans and Americans had died in Anjer was equally untrue. Another incorrect report, he pointed out, claimed that the dome of the ancient Hindu temple at Borobudur had been crushed by falling rocks. That place was situated three hundred miles from Krakatoa, McColl pointed out, and it had not been damaged.

The Rev. Tennyson-Woods, on his tour of Bantam in September, found "nothing left. Not a house, scarcely a tree, not a road," only a confused mass of earth, branches, trees, houses, household utensils, remains of human beings, clothing, stones and bricks, muddy flats and stagnant pools. At one spot he noticed a foot and a mass of hair sticking up from the mud, the only indication that a body lay there. Mr. Schuit, of Anjer, told him that it would be impossible for many years to rebuild the town; its neighbourhood was a wilderness and quite uninhabitable.

The Resident of Bantam informed the Governor-General on September 7th, that 1,517 bodies had been buried at Anjer, and a further 140 awaited burial. It was impossible to extricate them from the debris of houses and trees with which they were mixed, he said, and he asked for eight thousand cases of petroleum so that they could be burnt.

The Englishman from Chikandie Udik returned to his home on his release from the hospital, uttering this lament:

Poor Bantam, unfortunate country! When will your calamities end? Have you not suffered enough? Enough and more than enough. Disease had thinned our stock, fevers and other diseases had stricken the people. The crops had hardly met requirements. Our fate is sad, terribly sad. Under the fatherly protection of Government we were slowly but surely recovering from these blows, but what has now happened has blasted every hope and filled the mind with despair. The prospects of Bantam are now destroyed for good.

People living in Batavia, he said, could form no idea of how matters stood. The soil had become barren, the prospects were gloomy. The ground gave the appearance of a heavy snow-storm. It would never provide crops again.

This man's forebodings were too pessimistic. In time Bantam revived, to support an even greater population than before. The volcanic ash fertilised its fields. Krakatoa gave life as well as death.

Ten-year-old Yasim crept back to the village of Waluran, or rather to the place where it had stood. But nothing was left. He found his father's dugout canoe lodged in a broken tree. With the aid of some friends, he dragged it to the beach and launched it into the water. It was still seaworthy. With the canoe, Yasim revived his father's trade. As the years went by, and the village was repopulated by strangers, Yasim paddled into the Straits, selling fruit, parrots and monkeys to the crews of passing ships, seamen who were pleased to spend a few minutes listening to his tale of the great catastrophe. Yasim's experiences gave him a sort of glamour in his village. He married two wives, and had many sons; when the fish returned eventually to the Straits, the sons caught them, building up a considerable trade with the villages inland. They did so well that Yasim was able to give up work, sit outside his house, and tell and retell his story of the great eruption of Krakatoa to his grandchildren—who were "most impressed," he proudly informed his interviewer in 1956.

"Have you heard any news from the Lampongs?" was the question on every lip in Batavia as the days went by and no news came. The answer was usually a sorrowful shake of the head. The Government tug *Preanger*, despatched in the *Kederie*'s wake, was, like her, unable to reach Telok Betong;

but the *Preanger,* unlike the *Kederie,* became stuck in the pumice and was unable to proceed or return. Two other steamers were sent to Lampong and Semanka bays.

The *Graaf van Bylant* churned through miles of floating pumice, until her engines became clogged. Her captain was warned by Captain Hoen of the *Kederie* not to try to proceed further. The *Prins Hendrik,* a man-of-war of two thousand tons, carrying 229 Europeans and fifty-three natives, was more fortunate. She succeeded in reaching Vlakke Hoek, where her crew found that, of the lighthouse men, three Europeans were wounded and ten natives were dead. The vessel failed to reach the head of Semanka Bay for, where the sea was not covered by pumice, the breakers were too strong. Next day a boat, manned by a lieutenant and sixteen sailors, succeeded in reaching the shore, rescuing the Dutch officials, who had collected when they saw the warship. But when the vessel tried to leave the bay, she could hardly turn round. As far as the eye could see, the sea was covered with pumice. It got into the ship's engines, and the condenser exploded. It took thirty hours to repair it before the rescued survivors could be taken to Batavia.

When Mr. Struick finally reached the Lampongs, two weeks after the eruption, he reported to the Governor-General:

> Lampong Bay, formerly so picturesque, is wholly changed in appearance since the volcanic eruption. All the trees are dead. The hills and mountains have all the same pale yellow or dark grey colour. The shores both of the islands and mainland, to a height of 90 to 120 feet above sea level, are quite bare, and covered with a grey coloured muddy deposit probably left behind there by the tidal wave. Where formerly hundreds of white sails on fishermen's proas and other crafts were charmingly reflected upon the blue surface of the water, the only living creature now visible is a solitary water bird which wanders by itself along the greyish plain.

The Europeans at Telok Betong were entirely destitute, he reported. His only cheering news was that the mosquitos, which formerly infested the district, were gone. They had been destroyed by the ash and pumice, which threw a cloak over all stagnant water.

The chief inspector of beacons and lighthouses sent warships to patrol the Straits, to take soundings and warn shipping. They were joined by American and British naval vessels which were ordered to render assistance.

Captain M. C. van Doorn, the officer commanding the Dutch survey vessel *Hydrograaf*, was not surprised when the order came to sail to the Straits of Sunda, where he was told to rechart the area around Krakatoa. Anchored in Padang Harbour, Sumatra, he heard Krakatoa's roars on August 27th. Krakatoa had disappeared, and sixteen new volcanoes had arisen from the sea bed between the island and Sebessi, he was informed. The *Hydrograaf* reached Krakatoa on Thursday. The island, van Doorn saw, had not entirely disappeared, and no new cones were visible in its neighbourhood. The "new islands" were no more than low banks, smoking and steaming, which, seen from afar, could have suggested that fresh cones were in eruption. They were covered by hot pumice, which gave off clouds of steam as the high waves broke over them. They remained above the surface of the sea for some weeks, and they were named Steers and Calmeyer.

Reporting to the naval officer commanding at Batavia, van Doorn stated:

> The northern part of Krakatoa has entirely disappeared. At what is now the northern edge the peak rises nearly perpendicularly from the sea, and forms a crumbled and rugged wall, and shows a vertical cutting (which is more than 2,500 feet high) of Krakatoa.
>
> Where was land before, there is now no bottom to be found; at least we could not fathom it with lines of 200 fathoms (1,200 feet) long. When we had quite calm weather, and steamed slowly and cautiously to and fro along the base of the peak, or had turned off steam and let the ship drift, and were busy in measuring the depth, we could distinctly see the different strata and rocks of the bare, opened mountain. Only here and there a

slight trace of melted volcanic matter was to be seen, which, after half of the mountain had crumbled away, had flowed over the wall, which is still there. What remains of the slopes is covered with a greyish-yellow stuff (which, as plainly appears, had been in a melted or fluid state), full of cracks or splits from which steam is continually coming out.

In the same way, steam is also coming forth from the deeper cracks of the steep wall, which is still remaining. Sometimes this is accompanied by slight explosions; at that time clouds of brown dust fly up from the cracks, and stones roll down which are often so big as to disturb the sea around the entire base of the mountain. Our entire survey of the north of Krakatoa suggested the idea that we were above a crater which had been filled with water and quenched by it, and this idea was further strengthened on observing that the decrease of depth, south of Sebessi, had principally been caused by matters which were cast out and flung away.

Almost in every place the lead came up from the bottom, filled with black sand or carbonised dust sometimes mixed with pulverised pumice-stone and little black stones, which apparently had been in a red-hot or melted state. Moreover, the soundings were very different, and the new rocks resemble clods of substances which, when in a melted or very hot state, had contact with water. Probably such a whimsical shape of the rocks above the sea-level suggests the state of the bottom of the sea in the neighbourhood. The stones were still too hot to allow us to discover whether massive stones are under the pumice stone also. It was not difficult, it is true, to knock off large pieces of these rocks by a hatchet or a chopper, but when a big block fell unexpectedly down, the sailors often had to flee on account of the gases which suddenly arose. The broken-off pieces which were brought on board were still warm after they had been in the boat for an hour.

As is to be seen from the map, a great part of the lost ground of Krakatoa is found again at the bottom of the sea, a few miles to the north at least, if we suppose that no undulations of the ground took place. After having passed the limits to which the matters were thrown out, one finds the same soundings as were found before, and the decrease of depth is so local that the idea of an upraised bottom is dissipated at once. If such an elevation had taken place, it certainly would be remarked over a far greater extent and be more regularly ascending and descending. The firmer and stronger part of the crater wall, the peak of Krakatoa, which is still there, remained standing when the lower and feebler part dropped down, and the water found its way into the fearful boiling pool. We cannot wonder therefore about the quantity of steam that came forth (of which we are not able to form an idea), which caused a strong explosion. The movements of the sea which followed it caused tidal waves, the destroying force of which was experienced in such a fearful manner at the coast of Bantam and the Lampongs.

It is also worth mentioning that a change took place in the shape of Verlaten Island; the area is now triple what it was before, though it is plainly visible that large pieces of the beach were there knocked off a short time ago. Lang Island, in size and formation, has remained almost unaltered. The sight of these islands, which were formerly covered by a luxurious vegetation, is now very melancholy. They are now buried under a mass of pumice-stone, and appear like shapeless clods of burst clay (*i.e.* covered with cracks). After a torrent of rain, the coming forth of steam is sometimes so dense that these islands, when seen from afar, appear like hilly ground covered here and there with snow. When looking at these spots through telescopes, one can plainly see that these white specks are formed by a great number of clouds, which issued like steam from the fissures.

Sebessie is also covered with ashes up to the top, which appear like a greyish-yellow cloth. But it seems that the cover is already less thick here, for here and there one sees the stumps of dead trees peeping out from the crust. Sebokoe shows a dreadful scene of devastation. Perhaps all that lived here is not so completely destroyed as was the case on the southern islands, but the sight of the bare fields of ashes, alternating with destroyed woods, the trees of which are all either dead or uprooted, gives one a still better idea of the destructive powers which were here at work. It is not until we come to the small islands northward of Sebokoe that our eyes are gladdened by little specks of green.

Yet, within a month, noticed Captain van Doorn, the coasts of Bantam began to revive. The tropical rains washed away the ash, and fresh green grass reappeared. Even near the beach, young cocoanut and banana trees sprouted new shoots between the chaos of dead trees and broken rocks.

The *Koningin Emma der Nederlander,* with Lieutenant Tydemann on board, was sent to patrol the western end of the Straits, to warn shipping of the dangers of navigation. On the islands no green could be seen. Lang and Verlaten were covered with rock-grey pumice, streaked by ravines made by the great waves. The southern part of Krakatoa stood up like a gigantic tooth, perpendicular on its northern face, a feathery mass of dust streaming from its peak, and giving off a rumbling noise as rocks rolled down its slopes.

Roundabout on the coasts, as far as the eye could see, Tydemann says, the fields were grey with pumice, which made him think that the ship was grinding its way through a desert of blinding gravel. "One got an impression," he reports, "of the height and violence of the tidal wave and the gigantic whirl-pool formed when the crater blew up, by looking at the island of Thwart-the-way, on which countless trees had been up-rooted and carried to the height of 90 feet above sea-level, on seeing the shore near Anjer, a desert waste, where no houses stood, of masses of coral weighing many hundreds of tons, stranded inland, and by the sight of the lighthouse at Second Point, its thick steel-reinforced brickwork reduced to its foundations, its stones broken and scattered."

Yet in all this misery and barrenness there was a glimpse of beauty. Millions of brilliantly coloured butterflies, born in the ash, unable to find food, and lacking the strength to fly further afield, fluttered, searching in the watery surface for a dry spot on which to land. They swept over the sea, alighting on the warship in thousands, and rising again to turn and twist before falling to a watery grave.

The Queensland Royal Mail steamer *Cheyebassa,* coming from Australia, reached the eastern end of the Straits on September 2nd. Captain Morris described his experiences in a letter to an Indian newspaper:

The awful news did not reach until, I think, Wednesday, when a pilot came in whose wife had been washed up into a tree and left by the wave. He brought the intelligence that Krakatoa had disappeared and the channel blocked. Here was news for me to get! Fortunately, a Netherlands India steamer was expected from the Straits, and we only had to wait. She did not arrive till Saturday afternoon. The commander's report was something awful. The big channel remained clear, he believed, as he came through it, but it was strewn with huge trees, bodies, and fields of floating pumice. Pleasant, was it not, for us? Our agents suggested going by Singapore, but I argued that if one ship could get through I could. We were ready for sea on Saturday evening, but I did not leave till two on Sunday morning, so as to have good daylight all through the Straits. Well, at seven on Sunday morning, September 2, we opened the Straits, and the sight was painful—bare rocks, nothing else, ruin everywhere. Anjer, that we had so often admired, the site not even to be recognised, a small bit of the lighthouse foundation standing, nothing more, and the sea more dreadful still with its awful burden, steering here and there to avoid all kinds of things, no dangers apparent, which was to us the most important. At last we saw Krakatoa, only the principal peak left, the whole north part cut down perpendicularly, and gone clean away. It was still smoking in places where it had not been smoking previously, so I am much afraid there will be more mischief. It was a lovely day, and I was able to get a series of angles, from which I have made a chart. After passing Krakatoa things got thicker in the water, huge trees, roots and all, like islands, every conceivable thing that that awful wave could tear away. I got awfully anxious about this time. I could not find the man-of-war, and, night coming on, the thought of having to cruise all night in such company gave me the cold shivers. At last, at six, I saw her masts in under the land. By seven I had fulfilled my commission, and was away to sea, with a big load off my mind; starting fair wind behind me, I did not leave the deck that night, you may be sure, for fear of trees, which I hoped to make out by the water breaking against them. However, all went well. Daylight came in with a dull, blowy day and torrents of rain, but anything was pleasant after those awful Straits. I am curious to hear further reports at Aden, because that morning, at eleven, when quite 140 miles away, we heard a most tremendous report like a heavy peal of thunder, right in the direction of the Straits. If the rest of the island is gone, Heaven save the ships we left there!

Fortunately, Captain Morris was mistaken in thinking that Krakatoa was again active.

The *Norham Castle* parted company from the *Sir Robert Sale* after the two vessels entered the Straits. Due to call at Anjer, Captain Sampson stood for two days off the coast, and, seeing only devastation, he sailed on in the semidarkness, forging through banks of pumice and floating corpses. Unfamiliar with the changed coastline, Sampson ran the *Norham Castle* aground on Princess Island, from where his vessel was towed off by the American corvette *Juanita,* which had been ordered to break her voyage from Singapore to China to aid the Dutch navy. Captain Harrington told his men to give three rousing cheers as the *Norham Castle* refloated.

The floating dock, the *Volharding,* which went adrift on August 27th from Tanjong Priok, was cast ashore on September 3rd, down the coast from Batavia, from where she was refloated, none the worse for her eight-day voyage.

Several months elapsed before the Dutch could form any accurate estimate of the number of casualties caused by Krakatoa's eruption. When they were finally published, the figures disclosed that a total of 36,417 people had died, of whom thirty-seven were of European race. Of the villages and towns, 165 had been destroyed totally, and another 132 seriously damaged. Verbeek analysed these figures (see table, page 182).

There were a number of discrepancies in the official figures, points out Verbeek. Only the casualties amongst the Dutch were known accurately, he says. In all probability the deaths of natives, Chinese, Arabs and other "Asiatic foreigners" were higher, for countless bodies were carried out to sea by the retreating wave. The great number of deaths had been due to the inrush of the sea; only a few people had succumbed to burning ash and pumice, Verbeek learned on his tour of the devastated districts.

	Euro-peans	Asiatics	Villages entirely destroyed	Villages partly destroyed
SUMATRA				
Benkolen	—	34	2	—
(Vlakke Hoek and Kroe)				
Lampongs				
Town of Telok Betong	3	714	9	1
District of Telok Betong	—	1546	24	4
Sekampong	—	5	—	—
Kalimbang	1	8037	46	—
Semanka Bay	1	2159	23	31
JAVA				
Bantam				
Serang	—	1933	3	30
Anjer	14	7583	10	25
Merak	13	—	—	—
Tjaringin	5	12017	38	12
Batavia	—	2350	10	26
Krawang	—	2	—	3
	37	36380	165	132

Verbeek was ordered to investigate the cause of the eruption. He headed a Government mission of enquiry, composed of five members: Cartographer J. G. de Groot, Mining Inspectors J. F. Corte and C. W. Axel, and Sergeant-Major P. B. W. H. Schrenders, who made sketches and drew charts. The party sailed to Krakatoa on the *Kederie*, in command of Captain Hoen, reaching the islands on October 15th. The first voyage lasted seventeen days. Verbeek made four further visits to Krakatoa. His first task was to learn whether the volcano was still in eruption, as many observers declared. Minor explosions, he says, were heard for some months following the major outbreak. Irregular muffled sounds came from Krakatoa on September 17th and 26th, and on October 10th, and for several weeks clouds were observed streaming from the peak of Rakata. Even as late as February 20th and 23rd, 1884, the captains of ships navigating the Straits reported thunderous rumblings and flashes of light. Verbeek investigated these reports. Krakatoa, he says, continued to throw out mud for some time after the eruption, and these discharges may have been accompanied by minor explosions. The February manifestations he dismissed as hallucinations caused by electrical atmospheric storms.

It is not yet opportune to discuss Verbeek's final conclusions, other than his early discovery that, contrary to local opinion, the eruption had not been accompanied by violent earthquakes. Only a few places experienced earth shocks, and these were slight, Verbeek learned. The air near the island during the eruption had been hot and suffocating; barometers rose and fell repeatedly and irregularly, and electrical phenomena of great intensity had been observed. The reports that Radjah Bassa had been active were untrue.

Verbeek surveyed Steers and Calmeyer islands. He found that they were bare banks of pumice on which the sea was already encroaching. The heat given off by the pumice nearly stupefied him. Taking its temperature, he found it was 42° Celsius (107.6° F.). The white pumice, he noticed, was covered by a thin layer of fine black ash.

The party landed on Krakatoa, remaining there for two days. They climbed to the top of the crater and descended its steep face. What he saw astonished Verbeek. On the grey pumice, two black streaks were visible, beginning about seven hundred feet from the top, and they could be traced in a tolerably straight line down to within three hundred feet above the sea. They proved to be mud streams. They covered the white pumice to a thickness of nearly one foot and had a breadth of from three to fifteen feet. He saw clearly where these mud streams had flowed into deep ravines. It proved that they had not flowed until after the crevices had been formed by the rains, which followed several weeks after the eruption.

Verbeek collected numerous samples of pumice and rock,

including a number of round balls resembling marbles. He smashed several in order to learn their composition. They were calcareous lumps of marl. Layers of marl existed only at the bottom of the Straits, he knew. These balls came from deep beneath the volcano, and their situation on top of the ejected pumice showed they belonged to the last explosions.

Verbeek returned to Batavia, where he reported that there was no fear of further eruptions from Krakatoa. He set about the task of analysing the material he had collected. To the enquiries of his friends about the cause of the eruption he would say nothing. But he made what was to prove a remarkable prophesy:

> In any renewed activity of the volcano, it is to be expected that islands will arise in the middle of the sea basin that is surrounded by Rakata Peak, Verlaten Island and Lang Island . . . just as the craters Danan and Perboewatan formed in the sea within the old crater wall.

Other people were less cautious than Verbeek, as the Rev. Tennyson-Woods discovered. The volcano had "blown its head off," he was told. The cones of Perboewatan, Danan and half Rakata had been shattered by the great explosion into millions of pieces, and their debris had been distributed over the devastated area where it lay intermingled with the ash and pumice.

The French Government, by permission of the Governor of the Dutch East Indies, also sent a mission to explore Krakatoa. Messrs. Cotteau, Breon and Korthals reached Batavia on May 14, 1884, where a small steamer was placed at their disposal. They landed on the coast of Bantam, viewing its desolation and noting "a well-marked line, running at an elevation of from 50 to 80 feet above sea-level, indicating the limit of the terrible wave." They called at Telok Betong. "Here the extensive and thickly-settled coastland had assumed the aspect of the desolate swamp, relieved here and there by a few bamboo huts recently set up." They saw a vast plain of desolation, covered by pools of brackish water. A mark ninety feet high showed the passage of the great wave. Above this strip the rain of ash had continued the devastation by burning the leaves of trees, breaking their branches, and killing the vegetation.

The three members of the expedition were taken to see the remains of the *Berouw*, which they found straddling a stream, forming a makeshift bridge. All attempts to refloat the gunboat had failed and were useless, they were informed.

Leaving Lampong Bay, they visited Sebessi and Sebokoe islands, which were completely covered by dried mud, several yards thick, furrowed by deep crevices. In a village on Sebessi they saw the remains of from fifty to sixty skeletons, whitened by the sun, some still clad in gaily coloured sarongs. Several shining skulls still had clumps of hair attached. Everywhere, they noticed vigorous shoots of bamboo growing out of the ash.

When they reached Krakatoa on May 26th, the banks of Steers and Calmeyer had disappeared completely and were now covered by from twelve to fourteen feet of water. Verlaten Island was covered in ash and pumice, to a depth of one hundred feet, the French scientists estimated. The island was twice its former size and it looked like a glacier, to Cotteau.

As they neared Krakatoa Island they saw that its cone was enveloped in a plume of thick white cloud which caused them to think it was still active. Vapours arose from fissures all the way up to its 2,700-foot summit. Closer inspection disclosed the truth. Heavy stones and rocks were bounding down the mountain slopes, raising clouds of dust which they had mistaken for vapour. They raced down, making a noise that sounded like the rattle of distant musketry. A stone, the size of an orange, struck one of the sailors, ricochetting into the sea, as the party reached the island in a rowing-boat. When another rock, which Cotteau estimated to weigh thirty tons, flew past, they decided to retire. Surveying the island from a safe distance they noted, in the deep north wall, alternating streams of black and red lava, separated here and there by bands of up-flung strata. The depth of the sea bed where the cones of Perboewatan and Danan had formerly risen was now six hundred feet, the scientists learned from soundings. They were able to collect some samples of Krakatoa's eruption. These consisted of fragments of black and dark green glass, and spongy pumice which, upon analysis, disclosed a silica content of 72 percent. The extreme acidity of these eruptive products surprised the scientists, for, as they stated in their report to the French Minister of Public Instruction, "it proved the inaccuracy of the theory which claims that in a volcanic region, the eruptions are always succeeded in order of decreasing acidity."

Next day the members of the expedition succeeded in making a safe landing on Krakatoa. Everywhere they found a solidified bed of mud and ash, 200-260 feet thick. Cotteau explored a crevasse, finding in a crevice a microscopic red spider busily spinning its web, optimistically, he thought, for there was no other living thing on Krakatoa for it to catch.

The miracle had happened. Life had returned to the devastated island.

12. A Child Is Born

WITHIN twenty to forty years Krakatoa became recloaked in vegetation, and many species of birds, animals and insects were found living amidst its foliage and greenery. Most botanists and zoologists cite Krakatoa as the classic example of recolonization following destruction. But was all life on the island destroyed on August 26-27? One botanist, Professor C. A. Backer, does not think that is proved.

Before 1883 Krakatoa was a luxuriant mass of greenery, and the island was the habitat of numerous small animals, birds, rodents and insects, but no one knows exactly what species of flora and fauna lived there. The island had been uninhabited for many years. The crew of the *Discovery* encountered a few natives in 1780, and in 1809 a small penal colony was situated there. When Verbeek visited the island in 1880, it was covered in dense vegetation and deserted except for the occasional fisherman or woodcutter. After the great eruption the island was visited only spasmodically by Europeans, and twenty years elapsed before it was fully explored.

Verbeek, after his visit in October, 1883, was of the opinion that all life had been destroyed, telling Dr. B. M. van Leeuwen, many years later, "the old basalt surface was covered with a layer of pumice-stone and ashes; the ejected material was so hot that the coolies danced on their bare feet." Cotteau, of the French mission which landed in May, 1884, reported, "Notwithstanding all my researches, I was not able to observe any symptoms of life;" other than the red spider, of course. When Verbeek returned in August and September, 1884, he found only carbonised tree trunks. He came again in July, 1886, and

June, 1887, remarking on the last occasion some blades of grass rising through the ash.

The first botanist, Dr. Treub, director of the botanical gardens at Buitenzorg, landed on the island in 1886. He walked over its barren slopes and covered only a fraction of its surface on the northwest side. There he found 34 plant species (11 cryptograms, 5 monocotyls, 10 dicotyls), and he also saw plants growing near the summit. He concluded that all previous vegetation must have been destroyed. In 1887 young forests were observed in ravines, and tall and dense grasses and ferns were seen, all from afar. Every attempt to reach the summit failed.

Ten years later Botanist Penzig found 61 species and noticed 132 species of birds and insects. In 1906 Ernest collected 108 species of plants. Another visitor remarked a green mantle on Krakatoa's summit and a grove of trees on its shore, some of them from twenty to thirty feet high. C. A. Backer, 1906, found several ravines cloaked with trees, and he observed 137 new species of plants, trees and shrubs. The grass was so high he had difficulty in penetrating inland. Two years later he reached 1,200 feet, finding young forests, and seeing more fully developed trees higher up. In 1908 Dr. van Leeuwen, director of the Botanical Gardens, remarked the presence of 276 species, and in 1919 he was astonished to find such fully developed vegetation. Lizards, bats, pigeons, monitors, pythons, rats and cockroaches were seen between 1915-1917. By 1929 Krakatoa was fully recloaked in vegetation and inhabited by small wild animals.

How did they get there? Were they all imported or did some forms of life survive the holocaust of heat and ash? It is too easily assumed, suggested Professor Backer, that all life was destroyed in 1883. That Krakatoa's soil was thoroughly sterilised is not proven. The higher areas were not visited by the early botanists and it is possible that some species of plants, if not animal life, survived beneath the thin layers of pumice which covered the southeastern slopes of the volcano, where vegetation was still dense two weeks before August 26th. These layers were, he says, insufficient to have destroyed all roots, seeds, spores and bacteria. The southeastern side of Krakatoa's peak was sheltered from the volcano's blasts, the ejecta of which would have cooled at the great height which it reached in the atmosphere before it fell back on the island, unlike the fragments deposited at greater distance which, because of their lower angle of flight, remained hot. Heavy rain fell, Professor Backer points out, in the two "monsoon" months following the eruption.

Professor Backer cites the experience of a German named Johann Handl who obtained a concession in 1915 to win volcanic products from the island. He was not able to effect his purpose, but in the process of trying he dug several pits, finding beneath the layers of ash unburnt tree trunks. He also found good water at eighteen feet and he was able to cultivate a garden.

Dr. van Leeuwen is not sure whether all Krakatoa's new life was imported by flight, by wind, by flotsam and by animals which reached the island. "We shall never be able to prove that not a single seed or rhizome survived," he said in 1929. Some life may have been latent under the ash. All the plants found since then could have been carried and spread by animals or by wind, he agrees. The seeds of some may even have been carried on the feet of the early scientific visitors.

The question of the repopulation of the island is less debatable, for if forms of life survived the eruption, they would have found nothing to eat. The fauna now known to exist could have reached the island by flight, by swimming, or by carriage on other animals or on decayed tree trunks. The fact that no earthworms could be found in 1908 convinced Dr. D. W. Dannermann, director of the zoological museum at Buitenzorg, that all the island's fauna had been destroyed, and he remarks that while van Martens found four species of mollusc in 1867, only one species was seen in 1889; the rarity of a species which could have survived pointed to its total destruction. The sequence of life was re-established, believes Dannermann, in the following order (1) scavengers, (2) plant-feeders,

(3) predatory and parasitic. Nature's cycle was still not normal in 1929, he found; some species, lacking their natural enemies, had multiplied rapidly. There was an over-abundance of rats, and few pythons, whereas a few years before, the reverse had been the case; the explanation being, apparently, that the pythons ate the rats which diminished. Lacking sufficient food, the pythons declined; the rats returned—the pythons and rats waxing and waning as nature re-established its cycle.

Alligators swarmed on the islands. Thereby hangs a story. Professor van Bemmelen made many visits to Krakatoa during his long service in Java. Requiring to spend some time on the island, he and Mrs. van Bemmelen camped on Lang from where, each day, the professor paddled over to Krakatoa, taking his lunch with him. After her husband left, Mrs. van Bemmelen busied herself in the camp. Fully occupied with her tasks one morning, she was horrified to see several huge alligators climbing ponderously up the beach. She retired to higher ground. The cat-and-mouse game continued all day. When her husband returned in the evening, Mrs. van Bemmelen was standing at bay on the island's highest point, surrounded by snapping alligators. The professor drove them away. He was far too excited to listen to the story of his wife's trying day. "I have discovered additional proof of Krakatoa's engulfment," he announced, waving aside her protests. "The alligators are harmless. They are *only* hungry," he assured her.

Professor van Bemmelen's discovery is bound up with the question, "What happened at Krakatoa during those fearful twenty-two hours in which no human eye could penetrate the inky blackness?"

Verbeek established certain facts in 1885. Krakatoa Island, previously eighteen square miles, had been reduced by three-quarters. Eleven square miles of its surface, one and one-eighth cubic miles of its bulk, had disappeared. Two of its three cones, Perboewatan and Danan, had vanished and the peak of Rakata had been sliced in two, leaving a precipitous cliff on its northern face. Lang and Verlaten islands were greatly enlarged. The islet of Polish Hat was no more.

Where the main part of Krakatoa Island had formerly risen 1,400 feet above sea level, now there lay a cavity 900 feet deep; alongside it the sea bed, previously 122 feet, was now 500 feet in depth. Within the four-mile-wide caldera, filled by sea, rose a new rock, Bootsmansrots, its tip reaching out fifteen feet from the surface of the sea like a "gigantic club which Krakatoa lifts defiantly out of the sea," in Verbeek's words. Beside it, the sea bed was 600 feet deep.

Verbeek visited Krakatoa several times and he toured the whole disaster area, examining the materials ejected during the eruption. 95 percent of it was, he found, fresh pumice. 5 percent only comprised old rock, the debris of the vanished cones. 4.3 cubic miles of material had been thrown out by the volcano, he estimated; on the low side, it is thought. Of this ejecta, he calculated that 2.86 cubic miles fell within a radius of 9.3 miles, chiefly in the sea, and partly on Krakatoa, Lang and Verlaten islands, where the pumice lay in banks 100 feet thick. As the radius from the volcano increased, the pumice thinned out to 3–5 feet at 12 miles, 1 foot at 13–24 miles, and 2–8 inches at 31 miles.

This data provided one tremendous clue to the volcano's behaviour. Only 5 percent of its original rock had been found. Where had the rest gone? There were only two possible explanations. Either the old cones had been exploded into tiny particles or they had collapsed and been engulfed into the depths below.

Professor J. W. Judd, of the Royal School of Mines, London, president of the Geological Society and a scientist of immense standing and prestige, decided that Krakatoa had "blown its head off," scattering the displaced material over thousands of square miles of earth. His explanation of the mystery, published in 1888, was widely accepted, and this incorrect solution of what happened at Krakatoa is still often quoted.

Verbeek, with his first-hand knowledge of Krakatoa, recognised that the total disappearance of the major part of the island could be accounted for only by the collapse and engulfment theory, the "blow-out-cave-in" process, as Professor van

Bemmelen calls it. That was the only explanation which fitted the facts. Krakatoa, Verbeek realised, was a splendid example of the theory by which geologists explained the total disappearance of the old cone of Somma in the Vesuvian eruption of A.D. 79.

That two of Krakatoa's cones and half its peak fell into the depths below, after their support had been withdrawn by the drainage of the magma chamber, is now accepted by all geologists. That conclusion has been singularly confirmed by Professor van Bemmelen's deduction that the volume of pumice ejected, when recalculated as magma, closely approximates to the volume of material displaced by engulfment. In other words, the space existed below for three-quarters of the island to disappear without trace.

But what happened precisely between 1 and 11 a.m. on August 27? That is a far more difficult question to answer, for geologists are not unanimous in their answers.

An imaginative reconstruction is permissible. Verbeek drew several diagrams to guide us. They enable us to both "look down" on Krakatoa, as if from an airplane, and to see the island in profile, as from a ship alongside. First we see Krakatoa as it was before 1883.

Looking from above, we see three islands: Krakatoa itself, running from southeast to northwest, from it rising the three cones of Rakata, Danan, and Perboewatan, in that order. To our right, on the northeast, lies Lang Island, with the islet of Polish Hat beside it, and to our left, on the northwest, Verlaten Island.

Descending to eye level, we see from the west, the islands in profile. Verlaten is to our left; Krakatoa holds the centre of the stage; beyond it, Lang. From Krakatoa Island rise the three cones of Rakata (2,700 feet), Danan (1,460 feet) and Perboewatan (400 feet), reading from right to left.

Now we may imagine the main island in section, as if it has been sliced down the centre by a giant's hand. (The dotted line in Verbeek's diagram above the cones represents the contours of the hypothetical primaeval cone.)

Danan lies directly above the chimney leading to the magma chamber below. Perboewatan is also fed directly from the chimney, but Rakata is connected with it only by a fissure. In fact, as Verbeek learned, Danan and Perboewatan were the active vents on August 26-27.

Having established how Krakatoa looked before the eruption, we can try to reconstruct the course of events during those twenty-two terrible hours between 1 p.m. Sunday and 11 a.m. Monday.

When, at 1 p.m. Sunday, the constraining plugs burst, the gas-charged magma roared up the chimney, being expelled through the two active vents in a series of gigantic blasts, falling as pumice, chiefly into the sea, where it set up waves sufficiently powerful to wreak havoc on shore. This process of *whomph, puff,* continued for many hours, until the magma chamber became drained at a higher rate than it could be replenished from the depths below. A void began to form under Krakatoa's central cones. The roof of the magma chamber started to sag and cave in.

The first stage of the Grand Collapse began at 4.40 a.m. on Monday. Perboewatan and the whole northern part of the island shuddered and fell, its huge mass crashing into the abyss. The sea rushed in. There came a mighty roar. Outward from Krakatoa gushed a huge wave. It destroyed Anjer and submerged the coastline directly across the Straits from Perboewatan.

Another great blast roared from Krakatoa about two hours later. A second great wave struck Anjer. This eruption came, think geologists, from a submarine vent situated on the sea floor near where Perboewatan had stood. How this was discovered is explained later.

Danan continued, during the early hours of Monday, to eject vast quantities of pumice, and Rakata may also have been active. Meanwhile the process of collapse continued. As more and more magma was expelled, the roof of the chamber cracked and collapsed. Danan was shaking on its foundations and the base of Rakata became fractured and undermined.

At 10 a.m., the last supports crashed into the chasm beneath the island. They took with them the central portion, the area lying between Danan and Rakata, part of the sea bed to the west, and half of Rakata's cone, which slithered sideways into the boiling maelstrom of red-hot magma and frothing rocks. Danan itself remained standing, miraculously saved from destruction by one shaft of solid rock.

Into this seething vortex the sea poured. Millions of gallons of cold water struck thousands of tons of boiling rock and hot magma. The mixture exploded with catastrophic violence. The roar of sound and the wave of pressure rose into the atmosphere, fanning out to travel round the world, rising so vertically that they jumped over the area immediately surrounding the volcano.

Millions of gallons of sea were sucked into the chasm beneath Krakatoa. Around the shores of the Straits, the sea receded. From the raging vortex gushed an enormous wave. It rushed across the Straits, rising to 50, 100, 130 feet, and it roared on round the earth.

The final destruction of Danan was only delayed. Its remnant crashed into the depths at 10.52 a.m. when, believes Verbeek, another great explosion, almost as powerful as the Big Bang at 10.02 a.m., that came from Krakatoa. The final stage of collapse and engulfment was completed at 4.30 p.m., he thinks.

Let us examine Verbeek's diagrams again. Krakatoa now looked like this. Half only of the peak of Rakata still stands; the rest of the island and part of the sea bed to its west have fallen into the magma chamber, three miles below, perhaps. A circular caldera, a cauldron-shaped depression, four miles in diameter, has formed, six thousand feet deep in places. Where a few hours before there had been land, now the sea flowed. One pinnacle of rock, a fragment of Danan, rises from the sea floor, and it was named Bootsmansrots. Both Lang and Verlaten islands have been greatly enlarged by banks of pumice, and two great banks, Steers and Calmeyer, rise in the sea beyond Lang Island. Their life is short. Rakata itself has gained in size from the mass of pumice dumped on its shores.

Dr. C. E. Stehn (who pays tribute to the work of Verbeek and B. G. Escher) explains the geological reconstruction of the sequence of events thus: *

Must we regard, he questions, the great mass of pumice which lies one hundred feet deep on Lang Island, for example, as the result of a single explosion, the one at 10.02 a.m., or of several explosions? Was it ejected simultaneously with, or after the main explosion? Verbeek concluded, Stehn observes, that at 10.02 a.m. a mass of rock, which he estimated at one cubic kilometre (1,307,943 cubic yards), sank into the depths. The great wave followed the collapse of Rakata. Then came the terrific explosion. The previous explosions came from Danan and Perboewatan, thought Verbeek, because ejecta corresponding with the rocks of Rakata was found rarely.

On his visit to Krakatoa, Stehn observed that on Lang Island the mass of ejecta lay above the pre-1883 vegetation. He could see the stratification of the bank of pumice at a great distance. From its composition he drew this conclusion: "The difference in the structure of the deposit and the thickness of the strata are evidence of severe eruptions following each other in rapid succession, after long intervals of rest, during which even the finest part of the ejecta had time to settle."

Three layers in the pumice excited his interest. At 2.95 metres (9 feet 8 inches) above sea level there was a 10 cm. (25.4 inches) thick layer, cinnebar red in colour. The pumic could have gained that colour only by oxidisation, by contact with sea water. It followed, therefore, that this layer had been ejected from a submarine vent, through the sea. The position of this hypothetical vent was established close to Perboewatan, by the layers of this coloured pumice which Dr. Stehn found only on the northern profiles of Lang and Verlaten islands. Another fact convinced Dr. Stehn that he was right in locating it there. Intermingled with the cinnebar-red pumice were small fragments of old rock, identical to the rock of Perboewatan, and pieces of coral which could have come only from the sea floor.

---

* *Krakatau*, Fourth Pacific Congress, 1929.

Dr. Stehn examined the relief of the sea bottom between the three islands. He found two main basins, the first between Lang and Verlaten, having an average depth of 70 metres (230 feet), in which there were two hollows 120 metres (394 feet) deep; the second centrally situated, with a level bottom 270 metres (886 feet) deep, and from it two depressions extending east and south.

From these facts, Dr. Stehn drew these conclusions:

Krakatoa Island was destroyed by several subsistences, explosions and waves. The differences of stratification on the north of Lang and Verlaten, and the absence of stratification on the south of Lang and the west of Krakatoa, were so great, and the composition of the deposits so varied, it was impossible to explain the destruction of the island by a single explosion. Nowhere was it demonstrated that the collapses were preceded by explosions.

The great part of the ejecta on Lang Island, the dark mass of pumice which formed a solid bank, and was absent from Verlaten and Rakata, came from the subsistence of Perboewaten at 4.40 a.m.

A mighty mass of pumice was ejected at 10.02 a.m. It was deposited without any sorting and it formed the greater part of the one hundred feet cliffs of Verlaten and Rakata. The destruction of Danan by collapse at 10.52 ejected products which were distributed over all three islands, first heavy rocks, then light pumice.

The rocks of the old stratum, upon analysis, showed 62.76 percent SiO_2, except the remnants of Danan (Bootsmansrots) which were 63.22 percent. (Verbeek, we note, found ejected rocks on Rakata, in which the silica content was as high as 70 percent.)

No tertiary bedrocks were found, indicating that the volcano did not "blow up," or explode.

The ridge between the two deep sea troughs could be accounted for by two explosions and two subsistences.

Other geologists have remarked the picture of the island's history provided by the scarred face of Rakata. The long process by which the cone was built by ejection and accumulation can be observed in its strata, layer above layer, one of which, 30 cm. (76 inches) thick, formed of old, weathered soil, shows that the volcano remained dormant for a very long time. The old rocks of the early period of growth were found to contain 65 percent silica.

This reconstruction and analysis of Krakatoa's eruption leaves unexplained the genesis of the great wave, a question on which there is no scientific unanimity.

Verbeek established what appears to be the salient clue, that the wave which followed the explosion at 10.02 a.m. was preceded by a "negative" wave, a recession of the sea from the shore. The water, he thought, was "attracted," that is sucked into the vortex of eruption and then "repulsed." Captain Baker on the *W. H. Besse*, we recall, noticed a current "running in the direction of the volcano at the rate of 12 miles per hour." His observation suggests that the sea was drawn into the volcano and was then expelled, forming a gigantic undulation which moved across the narrow Straits, rising in height as it neared the shore. That theory was advanced by Professor Judd, who pictured the sea rushing into the craters, chilling their magma and causing a great explosion. Professor Howell Williams,* however, finds Judd in error, and he attributes the genesis of the great wave to a mass of pumice striking the water.

Captain W. J. L. Wharton, who examined the origin of the waves for the Royal Society's report published in 1888, was more cautious than Judd, but he was influenced by Judd's theory of the "decapitation" of Krakatoa's cones. There were two types of waves, suggests Wharton, long and short, the shorter coming at irregular and at much briefer intervals than the long ones. He puts the question of the genesis of the great wave thus:

> How the great wave was born, whether by large pieces of the mass of the island falling into the sea; by sudden submarine explosion; by the violent movement of the crust of the earth under

---

* "Calderas and Their Origin," *Dept. Geological Science* 25. 1941. University of California Press.

the water; or by the sudden inrush of water into the cavity of the volcano when the side (i.e. of Rakata) was blown out—must ever remain, to a great extent, uncertain.

The pressure gauge of the gasworks at Batavia is no uncertain evidence that the three large waves were intimately connected with the three major explosions, observes Wharton. The three largest movements, at 5.43, 6.57 and 10.18 a.m. were all connected with the highest waves recorded on the tide gauge at Batavia.

Wharton calculated, on the basis of the accepted formula for measuring the speed of sea waves over certain depths, that the great wave took 2 hours 30 minutes to cover the one hundred sea miles to Batavia from Krakatoa. It arrived between 12.15 and 12.36 p.m., and it left the volcano, therefore, allowing for five and one-half minutes difference in longitude, at about 10 a.m. The same wave reached Anjer in 37, Tjaringin in 30, Merak in 45 and Telok Betong in 61 minutes.

The next wave in the series reached Batavia two hours and two minutes after the first wave. That lapse of time was very remarkable under the circumstances, thought Wharton. Let us follow his reasoning, bearing in mind he believed with Judd that Krakatoa had exploded into fragments:

> If the wave was caused by any sudden displacement of the water, as by the falling of large masses of ejected matter, and huge fragments of the missing portions of Krakatoa, or by the violent rush of steam from a submarine vent through the water, it is hardly to be conceived that two hours would elapse before the following wave, the second of the series, started after it.
>
> If the supposition that the wave was caused by the opening of a great chasm in the earth, by the bursting of the sides of the hollowed Krakatoa, into which the sea rushed, could be maintained, a wave of long period might also be explained; but, though some such inrush must have occurred when the water flowed over the site of the island, to set up a long wave, as is now required, two things appear necessary:
>
> First, that the chasm was large enough to permit water to flow into it continuously for an hour at a rate sufficiently rapid to

cause a great lowering of the water level in the vicinity of the island, in order to set up a wave.

Secondly, that the first effect reaching the shore was a negative wave.

Now, the first supposition is so improbable that it certainly requires evidence before it can be adopted; and the second is contrary to the record of the Batavia gauge, which shows a distinct positive wave as the earliest phenomenon.

If, however, upheaval of the bottom of the sea, more or less gradual, and lasting for about an hour, took place, we should have a steady long wave flowing away from the upheaved area, which as it approached the shore would be piled up considerably above its normal height. Thus these waves of long period would be set up; and this would also account for the rapid current recorded by the ship *William H. Besse,* which is described as 10 miles an hour, though probably that is an exaggeration. The water would flow back on the motion ceasing.

If we now turn to the condition of the area round Krakatoa and compare it with the previous state of things, we find that upheaval has taken place over a large surface. Two entire islands have appeared where formerly the water was deep. Verlaten Island has been increased by two square miles, and extensive banks have been raised.

I should have been inclined to consider this as the sole cause of the great waves, more especially as it would entirely explain the somewhat remarkable fact that ships not far from the volcano at the time the wave was travelling from it, felt nothing of the stupendous undulation which rushed so far up the slopes of the hills.

We find, however, as will be seen when the eye observations at distant places are considered that, besides the waves of long period, which after travelling thousands of miles were not of sufficient height to attract much notice, waves were observed by eyewitnesses following one another at rapid intervals of from five to fifteen minutes, and of heights of from two to three feet, though, from their short duration, they were not marked upon the gauges.

These seem to demand another cause, and it appears to me that they may be due to the large masses of the island blown away by the force of the explosions and falling into the sea, or, possibly, to the sudden displacement of the water over a submarine vent.

The missing mass of Krakatoa may be roughly estimated to be at least two hundred thousand million cubic feet (200,000,000,-000). A fiftieth part of this mass dropping suddenly into the water would, by its displacement alone, furnish sufficient liquid to form a wave circle of 100 miles in circumference, 20 feet high, and 350 feet wide. The surrounding islands and shoals would, however, prevent a perfect circle being formed, and the wave might therefore be concentrated on certain parts of the arc, and be at some places higher than at others, varying according to the direction in which the masses fell. It has been remarked that this partiality of the waves was noticed.

I incline then to the opinion that the destructive waves in the Strait of Sunda were mainly due to these masses falling into the sea, or to sudden explosions under the sea after it flowed freely over portions of the former site of the island, possibly to both causes; but that the long wave which was recorded on so many tide gauges had its origin in upheaval of the bottom.

It does not appear unreasonable to assume that at the time of the great explosion of 10 o'clock, waves of both characters would be more or less synchronously formed.

I advance this hypothesis of the origin of the waves with some diffidence, but it appears to be not improbable from the known facts, and it would explain away some difficulties.

This scholarly discussion of the genesis of the waves leaves the mystery unexplained. It seems probable that the early morning, and even perhaps the great wave itself, were set up by enormous masses of pumice striking the sea, although it must be admitted that the theory of attraction and repulse, and Judd's picture of suction, chilling, and explosion, is more attractive, particularly to laymen unversed in technicalities.

One final question remains. Is it correct to describe Krakatoa's outburst as the earth's greatest and most terrible volcanic disaster? Clearly there may have been eruptions of great magnitude of which little or nothing is known.

In order to answer the question it is necessary to establish or reject certain possible yardsticks of magnitude. The number

of people killed by a volcanic eruption is no criterion, for it
may occur, as did the eruption of Katmai in 1912, at a spot
remote from human habitation. Nonetheless, an eruption's
effect on human existence provides some standard of comparison. Paroxysmal eruptions have certain factors in common,
the volume of matter ejected, the mass of material engulfed,
and the distances reached by pressure and sound waves, and
by dust clouds. Krakatoa's sea wave was a special feature,
because of the island's unique position.

Krakatoa's sound wave was heard at three thousand miles,
the pressure wave encircled the earth seven and a half times,
and the dust cloud permeated the atmosphere in both hemis-
pheres. 4.3 cubic miles of material were thrown out and 1.8
cubic miles of rock were engulfed. Several notable eruptions
can be compared with that of 1883.

Of the explosion of Merapi in 1006 we know nothing except
that it probably destroyed the ancient Hindu state of Mataram
in central Java. An even earlier eruption, in the Mediterranean,
which is believed to have occurred about 1400 B.C., may have
been the cause of the destruction of the "splendid civilisation"
of Minoan Crete, according to R. W. Hutchinson.* About that
year, he says, a great catastrophe befell the island, a catastrophe
of which there is no clear record in history, but one that is
marked by destroyed and abandoned cities and villages, and
from which the civilisation as a whole never recovered. The
next four hundred years were marked by slow decadence.

It has been suggested by several authors that Plato's story of
lost Atlantis may have been derived, through a garbled version
preserved by Egyptian priests, from the sudden submergence
of ancient Crete. There is no confirmatory evidence for this
supposition, but it is remarkable that the most celebrated flood
legend in Greece, that of the Thessalian Deucalion, is placed
in the year 1330 B.C. It may represent a confused folk memory
of the disaster which struck Crete about that time.

The theory of the volcanic destruction of Minoan Crete was

---

* *Prehistoric Crete*, Penguin, 1962.

first advanced by Professor Spyridon Marinatos, director of
the Greek Archaeological Service, in an article in *Antiquity*,
December, 1939. He expanded his thesis further in his magnificent book, *Crete and Mycenae*, 1960, in which he compares
the eruptions of the volcano Thera (often called Santorin)
within Krakatoa's outburst of 1883, to the latter's detriment.

That Thera, one of the Cycladic Islands, sixty-two miles
north of Crete, erupted catastrophically about 1400 B.C. has
been established by J. Fouqué, who found a prehistoric crater
83 square kilometres (32 square miles) in extent, and 600
metres (1,969 feet) deep. Pottery discovered in an overwhelmed settlement established that this eruption occurred
about that time. Pumice, ash, and a tidal wave from Thera,
believes Professor Marinatos, destroyed cities and towns in
Crete. The sea waves set up, he thinks, travelled across the
deeper sea bed (1,000 fathoms) much faster than did Krakatoa's wave across the shallow Sunda Strait (100 fathoms). It
rose to even greater heights and it swamped the town of
Amnisos, the harbour of Knossos, the Minoan capital. Knossos
itself and several inland towns were destroyed, Professor
Marinatos thinks, by earthquakes which accompanied the eruption. At Amnisos he found thick layers of pumice and fallen
walls which he believes were sucked inwards by blast or by
the recession of the sea. While there can be no doubt that the
eruption of Thera wreaked havoc on the Cretan coast, the professor's supposition that it caused the simultaneous destruction
of the entire Minoan civilisation is more debatable, for his
theory calls for the eruption to have been accompanied by
violent earthquakes, which both Verbeek and Fouqué reject.

Professor Marinatos is on surer ground when he compares
the material lost, "blasted away" and sunk at Thera, with
Krakatoa's vanished bulk. Thera lost, he says, thirty-three
square miles against Krakatoa's vanished area of eleven square
miles. Thera's eruption may thus have been of greater magnitude, though, of course, we know nothing, about its side
effects.

Geologists rank several other ancient eruptions in the same

catastrophic category as Krakatoa's. Crater Lake, in southern Oregon, one of the scenic wonders of the United States, is a caldera formed about 6,500 years ago by the eruption and collapse of the cone which has been named Mount Mazama, and which may have risen to 12,000 feet in altitude. The crater is 6 miles across and is 2,000 feet deep, far larger and deeper than Krakatoa's. Professor Howell Williams has calculated the total volume of ejecta as 10–12 cubic miles, and he believes that 17 cubic miles of the prehistoric cone disappeared. Only 2 cubic miles of its old rock has been found, which leads to the presumption that 15 cubic miles were engulfed. It is doubtful, however, exactly what occurred, for Professor Williams has calculated that there was only 5 cubic miles of space within the magma chamber. Not all of the cone's mass could therefore have become engulfed. More than half of it must have been blown off in shattered fragments.

The eruption of Tambora in Java in 1815 must have been of similar magnitude to that of Krakatoa sixty-eight years later. It caused the death, directly and indirectly, of more people, and it brought complete darkness over an area of three hundred miles for three days. Its dust cloud had similar effects on the world's weather. The quantity of material ejected and engulfed is doubtful, and the former has been variously estimated from 28.6 to 10 cubic miles.

The eruption of Coseqüina in Nicaragua on January 20, 1835, has been examined by Professor Howell Williams, who describes it as the most violent historic eruption in the Americas. Its outburst lasted three days and its noise was heard as far away as Kingston, Jamaica, 850 miles distant. Ash fell over an area of 1,700 miles in diameter. One of the volcano's blasts was so terrible that "300 of those who lived in a state of concubinage were married at once" at one village. A caldera one and one-half miles in diameter was formed. Professor Williams estimates the ejecta at ten cubic miles and he thinks five cubic miles of rock vanished.

Comparison of Krakatoa with the famous eruption of 4,430 feet high Mount Pelée in Martinique on May 8, 1902, is unrewarding, for the tragedy which struck the town of St. Pierre, five miles away, is unique in the annals of volcanology. When superheated steam rushed up the chimney at 7.50 a.m., it found its outlet blocked by a stiff plug. It blasted out a vent on the side of the cone, directly facing St. Pierre. A hurricane of hot dust and gas, estimated at a temperature of 1200° C, shot at St. Pierre at a velocity of 100 miles per hour. All was over at 7.52 a.m. Thirty thousand people lay dead, asphyxiated by fumes and scorched by heat. The town was destroyed totally. There were only two survivors, a prisoner in an underground dungeon, and a shoemaker who escaped miraculously, apart from some of the crews and passengers on two steamers which, torn from their moorings, were blown out to sea. The glowing gas cloud destroyed an area of eight square miles. By a curious coincidence, the volcano Soufrière, on the island of St. Vincent nearby, erupted on May 6th. Pelée erupted again between 1929 and 1932, and the one thousand new inhabitants of rebuilt St. Pierre were evacuated.

Professor R. F. Griggs,* describes the eruption of Mount Katmai on June 6, 1912, thus: If the volcano had been situated at Vesuvius, near Naples, its explosion would have been heard in London, Paris, Berlin and Oslo. If the eruption had taken place in New York, the whole city would have been buried under one foot of ash, its population destroyed by hot gases. Philadelphia would have been covered for sixty hours in inky darkness, and the sound of the explosion would have been heard at Atlanta and St. Louis. As it was, no one was killed in sparsely populated Alaska when the volcano exploded without warning. Five cubic miles of matter was ejected and ash fell at Vancouver, 1,300 miles away. The top of the cone collapsed, leaving a crater two and one-half miles in diameter and 2,000–3,700 feet deep. The amount of material engulfed is estimated at just over one cubic mile.

Professor Grigg's similes suggest the employment of the same device for 1883. If we place Krakatoa at New York, the

---

* *The Valley of Ten Thousand Smokes,* National Geographical Society, 1922.

Big Bang could have been heard in both London and San
Francisco, depending upon the direction of the wind, three
thousand miles in either direction. Three-quarters of the area
of the island of Manhattan, to the height of the most lofty sky-
scraper, slanting downward from 1,460 feet at Central Park to
400 feet at the Battery, would have disappeared without trace
in the engulfment of Krakatoa's cones.

Comparison of these volcanic eruptions with Krakatoa's
famous outburst is inconclusive. Insufficient is known of them
to decide whether or not Krakatoa's eruption is the greatest
of historic times. It may well have been. Krakatoa was a small
mountain, yet it generated greater power than did larger cones
which, naturally, ejected or lost more material. Without reliable
data, we may agree with Professor Fred M. Bullard * who calls
Krakatoa's outburst "one of the greatest volcanic eruptions of
historic time, perhaps the greatest of all."

The story of Krakatoa's activity is not yet finished. On June
29, 1927, fishermen sailing between the three islands noticed
gas bubbles rising from the sea and at night they saw a red
glow. They informed the Dutch volcanological watching service, which had been set up in 1919 to safeguard the archipelago
from catastrophies similar to that of 1883. When geologists
reached the islands they saw steam issuing from the sea at a
spot above the wall of the northeastern rim of the caldera
formed in 1883, at a position midway between where the cones
of Danan and Perboewatan had formerly risen, where the sea
was six hundred feet deep.

Was Verbeek's amazing prophesy now to be fulfilled? So it
proved. Krakatoa was active again after forty-four years of
quiescence, in exactly the way the old geologist had forecast.
Between December 29, 1927, and February 5, 1928, an island
appeared, measuring 10 feet high and 600 feet long. It disappeared and reappeared several times. On February 3rd and
4th, 11,791 explosions were counted and on June 25th, 14,269

---

* *Volcanoes, in History, in Theory, in Eruption,* University of Texas Press,
Austin, 1962.

eruptions were seen. Dense clouds of debris and steam rose into the air, as is depicted in the photographs taken at 6-second intervals in January, 1928. The new vent remained submarine until October, 1952, when, after a number of vigorous explosions, a cinder cone emerged 200 feet above the sea. It was named Anak Krakatoa, "Child of Krakatoa." By March, 1953, its cone measured 330 feet, and in 1959 a new cone formed within its crater.

The island is now three thousand feet long and one thousand five hundred feet wide, and vegetation is sprouting on it. It was examined in January, 1960, by a twelve-man team, headed by Robert W. Decker and Djajadi Hadikusumo, which observed that the island was built from pyroclastic material, fine ash and larger blocks, erupted from six hundred feet below sea level, churning its way to the surface. The energy released by the larger individual eruptions is equivalent to the power of 170 tons of TNT. The team of scientists watched turbulent clouds of steam mushrooming up to three thousand feet.

Invited to give their opinion on the dangers arising from the new vent, they reported the unlikelihood of another caldera collapse for many hundreds of years, for the composition of the ejected material was still basaltic, and it showed no marked increase in silica. At its present rate of growth, Anak Krakatoa, they estimated, would require at least six hundred years to replace the volume lost in 1883.

Krakatoa's third volcanic cycle has started. Deep beneath the island the Demon is stirring. It is neither dead nor asleep. The volcano is not extinct. Many hundreds of years hence it may grow into a mighty mountain. The end of the volcano's first cycle may have been watched by very primitive men. Its second grand collapse was experienced by men on the threshold of knowledge. Who, or if anyone at all, may witness its third great paroxysm, is anyone's guess.

Geologists remark Krakatoa's famous outburst as a splendid example of the formation of a caldera by collapse and engulfment. We may describe it as a great human tragedy, probably the most terrible volcanic disaster that has been suffered by men.

One final word. On February 28, 1942, the Straits of Sunda reverberated again to the roars of explosion. This time, it was the real thing. Following the battle of the Java Sea on February 27, six allied warships, the U. S. cruiser *Houston,* the Australian cruiser *Perth,* the Dutch destroyer *Evertsen,* and the British ships *Exeter, Pope* and *Encounter,* sailed for the Straits, encountering a Japanese fleet. The *Houston, Perth* and *Evertsen* sank within sight of Krakatoa.

Bibliography

Abbot, C. G. and Fowle, E. E., "Volcanoes and Climate," *Smithsonian Miscellaneous Collections*, Vol. 60, 1913.

Ashdown, E., "A Floating Lava Bed," *Nature*, XXIX, 1883; XXX, 1884.

Backer, C. A., *The Problem of Krakatoa as Seen by a Botanist*, Batavia, 1929.

Bealby, J. T., "The Java Eruption and Earthquake Waves," *Nature*, XXIX, 1883.

Bemmelen, R. W. van, *Geology of Indonesia*, Vol. IA, Hague, 1949.

———, *The Influence of Geological Events upon Human History*, Hague, 1956.

———, Volcanic Tectonic Collapse Structures in Sumatra and Java, Lecture, 1961.

Berg, N. P., "Vroegere Berjchten Omtrent Krakatau. De Uitbarsting Van 1680." *Tijdsch van Ind. Taal-Land-en Volkenkunde*. Deel XXIX. blz., Batavia, 1884.

———, Dag Register Van Het Kasteel Batavia 1679, 1680, 1681, and Record of Ship *Aerdenburg*, June 12, 1680.

Bezemer, *Volksdichtung aus Indonesia* (Legend of Dajang Sambi and Sangkuriang), Hague, 1904.

Boutelle, C., "Water Waves from Krakatoa," *Science*, III, 1884.

Bréon, R. and Korthals, W. C., "Sur L'Etat Actuel du Krakatau," *Compte Rendu*, Vol. XCIX, 1884.

———, "Rapport sur Une Mission Scientifique dans le Detroit de la Sonde," Arch. d. Miss., *Science*, XII, 1885.

Bullard, F. M., *Volcanoes, in History, in Theory, in Eruption*, Austin, Texas, 1962.

Cotteau, E., "A Week at Krakatoa," *Proceeding of Royal Society of Australasia*, Vol. II, 1885.

COTTEAU, E. and KORTHALS, W. C., "Mission Francaise au Krakatau," *Compte Rendu, Soc. Geog.*, XV, 1884.

DALBY, R. J., "The Krakatoa Eruption in 1883," *The Listener*, 17 March, 1937.

DANNERMANN, K. W., *Krakatoa's New Fauna*, Part III, 4th Pacific Congress, Batavia, 1929.

DECKER, R. W. and HADIKUSUMO, D., "Results of 1960 Expedition to Krakatoa," *Journal Geophys. Res.*, Vol. 66: No. 10, 1961.

DIVERS, E., "The Remarkable Sunsets," *Nature*, XXIX, 1884.

DOORN, M. C. VAN, "The Eruption of Krakatoa," *Nature*, XXIX, 1884.

FLAMMARION, C., *Les Eruptions Volcan et Les Tremblements de Terre*, Paris, 1902.

FOUQUE, J., *Santorin (Thera) et Les Eruptions*, Paris, 1879.

FORBES, H. O., "The Volcanic Eruption of Krakatoa," *Proceeding of the Royal Society*, VI, 1884.

GENTILLI, J., "Present Day Volcanicity and Climatic Change," *Geog. Mag.* 85:172, 1948.

GLASSTONI, S., *The Effects of Nuclear Weapons*, U. S. Atomic Energy Commission, 1957.

HEILPRIN, A., *Mount Pelée and the Tragedy of Martinique*, New York, 1903.

HESSE, ELIAS DE, *Drie Seer Aanmerkelyke Reysen na en Door Velerley Gewesten in Oost-Indien; Elias de Hesse, Christopher Frike, Berghscnyver, Christophus Schweitzer. Yeder by Sonder, Vant Jaer 1675 tot 1686*, Vertaald door Simon de Vries, Utrecht, 1694.

HOPKINS, G., "The Remarkable Sunsets," *Nature*, XXIX, 1884.

HUMPHREYS, W. J. H., "Physics of the Air," 1940.

HUTCHINSON, R. W., *Prehistoric Crete*, Penguin, 1962.

JUDD, J. W., "Krakatoa," *Proceeding of the Royal Society*, May 1884.

————, "The Earlier Eruptions of Krakatoa," *Nature*, XL, 1889.

KENNEDY, H. G., "Report from H. M. Consul, Batavia, including Extract from Log Book of Steamship G. G. *Loudon*," *Proceeding of the Royal Society*, XXXVI, 1884.

LE CONTE, J., "Atmospheric Waves from Krakatoa," *Science*, III, 1884.

LEEUWEN, W. M. VAN, *Krakatoa's New Flora*, Part II, 4th Pacific Science Congress, Batavia, 1929.

LOBLEY, J. L., *Mount Vesuvius*, London, 1889.

MANLEY, W. R., "A Green Sun in India," *Nature,* XXVIII.

MARINATOS, S., "The Volcanic Destruction of Minoan Crete," *Antiquity,* Dec. 1939.

———, *Crete and Mycenae,* Thames & Hudson, 1960.

MASKELYNE, M. STORY-, "The Remarkable Sunsets," *Nature,* XXIX, 1884.

H.M.S. *Magpie,* Log Adm. 53/12,002. Public Record Office, London.

H.M.S. *Merlin,* Log Adm. 53/14540. Public Record Office, London.

METZER, E., "Gleanings from Reports Concerning Eruption of Krakatoa," *Nature,* XXIX, 1884.

MITCHELL, JR., J. MURRAY, "Recent Secular Changes of Global Temperatures," *Annals of N. Y. Academy of Sciences,* Vol. 95, Oct. 15, 1961.

PADANG, NEUMANN VAN, *Catalogue of the Active Volcanoes of the World,* I, Indonesia, International Association of Volcanology, Naples, 1951.

PERRET, FRANK A., *The Vesuvius Eruption of 1906,* Carnegie Institution, 1924.

———, *The Eruption of Mt. Pelée 1929–1932,* Carnegie Institution, 1935.

SANDICK, VAN, "Eruption du Krakatau," *Cosmos.* VIII, 1884.

STEHN, C. E., *Geology and Volcanism of Krakatoa Group,* Part I, 4th Pacific Science Congress, Batavia, 1929.

SYMONS, C. J., "The Eruption of Krakatoa," *Royal Society Report of Krakatoa Committee,* 1888.

THOMPSON, CAPTAIN, "Extracts, Log of *Medea,*" *Nature,* XXX. 1884.

TRUBNER'S AMERICAN AND ORIENTAL LITERARY RECORD (1865–1891), *The Krakatoa Eruption and Java Chronicles,* 1891.

TYRELL, S. W., *Volcanoes,* London. 1931.

VERBEEK, R. D. M., "The Krakatoa Eruption," *Nature,* XXX. 1884.

———, *Krakatau* (Dutch and French Ed.), Batavia, 1886.

———, *Krakatau Atlas,* Brussels, 1886.

VEREKER, CAPT. HON. F. C. P., "Extracts from Log of H.M.S. *Magpie,*" *Proceeding of the Royal Society,* XXXVI, 1884.

VOGEL, JOHAN WILHELM, *Journal Einer Reise aus Holland nach Oost-Indien,* Frankfurt and Leipsig, 1690.

WALKER, CAPTAIN, "Extracts from Log of the *Actea* (May 20, 1883)," *Nature,* XXX, 1884.

WATSON, CAPT. W. J., "The Java Disaster," *Nature,* XXIX, 1883.

WESTON, E. R., "Atmospheric Waves from Krakatoa," *Science*, III, 1884.

WEXLER, H., "On the Effects of Volcanic Dust on Insolation and Weather," *Bulletin* American Meteorological Society, Vol. 32, No. 1, Jan. 1951.

———, "Spread of the Krakatoa Dust Cloud," *Bulletin* American Meteorological Society, Vol. 32, No. 2, Feb. 1951.

WILLIAMS, HOWELL, *Calderas and Their Origin*, University of California Press (Dept. of Geological Science, Vol. 25, 1941).

———, *Crater Lake, the Story of Its Origin*, University of California Press. 1951.

———, *The Great Eruption of Coseguina, Nicaragua, in 1835*, University of California Press (Dept. of Geological Science, Vol. 29, No. 2, 1952).

NEWSPAPERS
1883–1884

Algemeen Dagblad, Bataviaasch Handlesblad, Java Bode, Javasche Courant, Locomotief, Tong-Tong.

Niew Padangsch Handlesblad, Niewe Rotterdamsche Courant, Niews Van Der Dag (New York).

Ceylon Observer, Ceylon Times, London and *China Telegraph, Scotsman, Singapore Times, Sydney Morning Herald.*

Acknowledgments

I EXPRESS my gratitude for the assistance given to me by the following institutions and individuals, none of whom are responsible for anything I say in this book:

The Royal Society; The Royal Geographical Society; The Geological Society of London; The Department of Geology and Mineralogy, University Museum, Oxford; The Hakluyt Society; The Zoological Society of London; The Royal Botanical Gardens, Kew; The General Register and Record Office of Shipping and Seamen, Cardiff; The British Broadcasting Corporation; The Meteorological Office; The Ministry of Defence; The First Secretary for Press Affairs, Royal Netherlands Embassy, London; The Press Attaché, Embassy of the Republic of Indonesia, London; The United States Department of Commerce, Weather Bureau; The Boston *Globe*; The Boston Public Library; Nederlands Genootschap voor Anthropologie; Koninklijk Instituut voor Tropen; Koninkluke Bibliotheek; Geologisch Instituut Der Rijksuniversiteit Te Utrecht; Geologisch Laboratorium Der Technische Hogeschool, Delft; Professor R. W. van Bemmelen; Mrs. van Damm; Dr. Neumann van Padang; Commander Frans Visée and Mr. Brian Daley (lecturer in geology at Portsmouth Technical College).

I acknowledge with many thanks the permissions granted to quote from the following publications: *Tong Tong*, May–July 1960, *The Eruption of Krakatoa, 1888*, and the *Bulletin* of the American Meteorological Society, January and February 1952.

Index

215

Index   **219**